Test Your Bridge Play

Edwin B. Kantar

100 Declarer-Play Problems Designed to Improve Your Card Playing Techniques

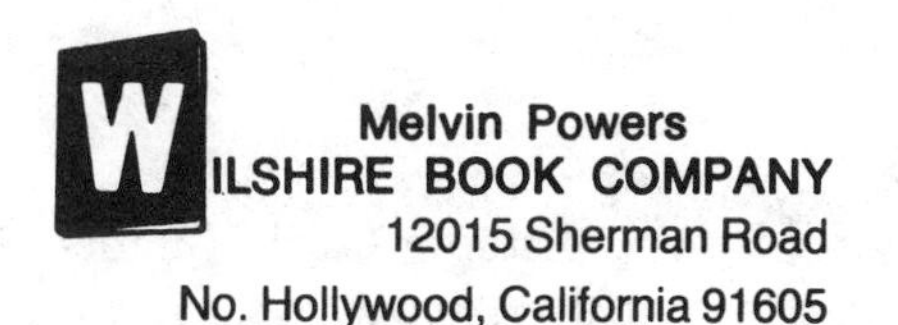
Melvin Powers
WILSHIRE BOOK COMPANY
12015 Sherman Road
No. Hollywood, California 91605

Library of Congress Catalog Card Number: 74-84310
ISBN 0-87980-286-3
Printed in the United States of America

FOREWORD

For twenty years I have been composing "Test Your Play" problems. The majority have appeared in: (1) newspaper columns, (2) Popular Bridge, (3) The American Contract Bridge League Bulletin, and (4) The Bridge World.

For obvious reasons, problems that appear, for example, in "Bridge World" are going to be much tougher than those appearing in a newspaper column.

What I have tried to do is to dig up 25 of my best problems from each of the four sources mentioned above to put together this 100 problem quiz book.

The first 25 problems should be the easiest because they have appeared in my column, the next batch of 25 are taken from Popular Bridge, a beautiful bi-monthly catering to the masses. The third group come from the A.C.B.L. Bulletin, a magazine which is mailed monthly to the 300,000 or so tournament players who belong to the American Contract Bridge League. Beware of the Bulletin problems. They are not easy. Finally, the last group of 25 have appeared in "Bridge World", a magazine with a world-wide reputation for catering to experts! You can imagine what to expect from those!

Bidding is given on most hands, particularly where adverse bidding might affect the play. On some hands you are in such wild contracts that the bidding is better left unseen, and on a few others it is so routine it is also excluded.

There is a rating scale at the end of each section of 25 hands and a grand finale rating scale at the end of the book, so keep score! Take five points for each of the first fifty problems and ten points for each of the last fifty. If you turn up with a low score, just don't mention it to anybody.

Incidentally, many of the hands in this book have been botched by some pretty fine players. So if you have an "accident" or two you are in good company. Good luck and don't worry about overtricks!

EDWIN KANTAR

Los Angeles

CONTENTS

Section I. COLUMN HANDS

A GIFT 1
DON'T BLOW THIS ONE 3
WRONG CONTRACT 5
CHILD'S PLAY 7
TAKE OFF YOUR SHOES 9
SIMPLICITY 11
THINK POSITIVELY 13
INSURANCE 15
THEY'RE NEVER COLD 17
SAFETY FIRST 19
THINK! 21
IT ALWAYS SEEMS LIKE A GUESS 23
DETECTIVE WORK 25
IT'S A LOCK 27
PERCENTAGE PLAY 29
IS WEST KIDDING? 31
JEWELS 33
100% 35
FOR YOUR LIFE 37
OUT OF THIN AIR 39
PLAY TO MAKE 41
GOOD DUMMY 43
DEUCES 45
CONFIDENCE BUILDER AND DESTROYER 47
A BAD BREAK 49
RATING SCALE 50

Section II. POPULAR BRIDGE HANDS

SO MANY FINESSES 51
PLACING HONORS 53
WRONG CONTRACT 55
DELICACY 57
CONSERVATION 59
CAUTION 61
HANG LOOSE 63
BLOCKS 65
CAREFUL! 67
MAYBE YOU'LL GET LUCKY 69
WHAT A DUMMY 71
BEHIND THE EIGHT BALL 73
SPOTS 75
WHAT CAN HAPPEN? 77
WHICH ONE? 79
OUCH 81
LOOKS EASY 83
IS IT A GUESS? 85
HANDLING A RUFF-SLUFF 87
INHUMANITY 89
STICKY, STICKY 91
OPTIMISM 93
A LITTLE SHAKY 95
FREE FINESSE? 97
EIGHT EVER NINE NEVER 99
RATING SCALE 100

Section III. BULLETIN HANDS

TECHNIQUE ... 101
WHERE THERE'S A WILL ... 103
CONFUSING ... 105
NINE OH NINE ... 107
LOOKING AHEAD ... 109
NO WAY OUT ... 111
FINE CONTRACT ... 113
A BEAUTIFUL HAND ... 115
WHAT IF? ... 117
SHAKY SLAM ... 119
INFERENCE ... 121
A STINKER ... 123
KING-JACK MISSING ... 125
MANAGEMENT ... 127
DREAM HAND ... 129
NOBLESS OBLIGE ... 131
HANDLE WITH CARE ... 133
TEMPTATION ... 135
ALMOST RIDICULOUS ... 137
NO SUPPORT ... 139
SURE THING ... 141
AMBITIOUS ... 143
TO FINESSE OR NOT TO FINESSE ... 145
THE CRYSTAL BALL ... 147
IMPENDING DOOM ... 149
RATING SCALE ... 150

Section IV. BRIDGE WORLD HANDS

FAVORABLE LEAD 151
FINESSES IN ALL SUITS 153
CONTROL YOURSELF 155
HOW DID WE GET THERE? 157
PLAY COOL 159
LOOKS EASY 161
SKILL TESTER 163
A TOUCHY GRAND 165
BRAVE RAISE 167
LOOK CLOSELY 169
VISUALIZE 171
CONSERVATIVE BIDDING 173
TWO TEN CARD FITS 175
TWENTY-EIGHT POINT SLAM 177
GREED 179
AWKWARD 181
TWO PARTS 183
TWO SUITER 185
RED KINGS IN THE SUNSET 187
NEVER A LAYDOWN SLAM 189
A PUZZLEMENT 191
TOO GOOD TO BE TRUE 193
KING-SIZE PROBLEM 195
THE MEN FROM THE BOYS 197
THIRTY-THREE POINTS USUALLY
PRODUCE A SLAM 199
RATING SCALE 201
GRAND FINALE RATING SCALE 201

Section I

COLUMN HANDS

A GIFT

North

♠ A J 7 6
♥ 3 2
♦ A Q 7 6
♣ K 9 4

South

♠ K Q 10 9 8 5
♥ K J
♦ K
♣ 6 5 3 2

Contract: 4 ♠

Opening lead: Jack of diamonds

Don't blow this one.

Solution

North
♠ A J 7 6
♥ 3 2
♦ A Q 7 6
♣ K 9 4

West
♠ 2
♥ A Q 9 8
♦ J 10 9 8 5
♣ Q 10 8

East
♠ 4 3
♥ 10 7 6 5 4
♦ 4 3 2
♣ A J 7

South
♠ K Q 10 9 8 5
♥ K J
♦ K
♣ 6 5 3 2

The only way to go down on this hand is to have a mental lapse or a complete collapse. There are ten tricks for the taking and even though a well-known expert did go down on this hand, you shouldn't.

Simply win the king of diamonds, draw as many trumps as necessary ending on the table, discard two *hearts* on the two good diamonds and eventually lead up to your king of clubs. If West has the ace you make an overtrick, if East has the ace you make your contract.

The only way to mangle this one is to discard clubs on the diamonds and then try to hold your club and heart losers to three tricks. That won't always work but the recommended play will.

DON'T BLOW THIS ONE

North

♠ Q J 9 8
♥ A 4
♦ Q 8 6 5
♣ A Q 3

South

♠ A K 10 3 2
♥ K Q 5
♦ J 7 4
♣ 5 4

Contract: 4 ♠

Opening lead: Deuce of clubs

West is a player who loves to underlead kings. How should South play this hand with the club lead?

Solution

North

♠ Q J 9 8
♥ A 4
♦ Q 8 6 5
♣ A Q 3

West

♠ 5 4
♥ 10 7 3 2
♦ A 10 9
♣ 10 8 7 2

East

♠ 7 6
♥ J 9 8 2
♦ K 3 2
♣ K J 9 6

South

♠ A K 10 3 2
♥ K Q 5
♦ J 7 4
♣ 5 4

Don't tell me you went for that con job about kings. You shouldn't finesse that club unless West flashes the king, and even then you had better have 20/20 vision. You have a surefire play (unless trumps are 4-0) by winning the ace of clubs, drawing trumps, discarding a *club* on your long heart and then exiting with a club. Whoever wins the trick will either have to give you a ruff-sluff or break the diamond suit — either one presents you with your contract. There is no bonus in this quiz, by the way, for taking practice finesses.

A practice finesse is a finesse, which, if it works, gives you the same number of tricks you would have taken had you not taken the finesse!

WRONG CONTRACT

North

♠ 5
♥ A 10 9 6 4 2
♦ A K 5
♣ 10 8 3

South

♠ K J 3
♥ Q J
♦ Q J 6 4
♣ A Q 9 4

Skillfully avoiding the laydown contract of 4♥, you have once again stolen the hand from your partner and are declaring three no trump.

West leads the six of spades and East produces the ten. Plan the play.

Solution

North

♠ 5
♥ A 10 9 6 4 2
♦ A K 5
♣ 10 8 3

West	East
♠ A Q 9 6 2	♠ 10 8 7 4
♥ 8 5	♥ K 7 3
♦ 8 7 3 2	♦ 10 9 8
♣ J 2	♣ K 7 6 5

South

♠ K J 3
♥ Q J
♦ Q J 6 4
♣ A Q 9 4

Your best bet is to work with clubs, not hearts. Three clubs will give you nine tricks, and taking two finesses through East should give you three club tricks approximately 75% of the time, at the same time keeping East out of the lead for a fatal spade play through your king. The heart finesse is strictly for dreamers.

Win the spade jack, cross to the ace of diamonds and run the eight of clubs. Assuming this loses to the jack, win any red suit return in dummy and run the ten of clubs. If this loses to the king, ask West why he didn't bid with the king-jack of clubs and the ace-queen of spades. Then ask your partner why he didn't correct your three no trump to a cold four hearts. In other words, keep the table off balance before your partner starts in on you.

CHILD'S PLAY

Neither side vulnerable

Dealer East

North

♠ A 7 6 4 3
♥ None
♦ 7 5 4
♣ A J 7 6 4

South

♠ K Q J 10 9 2
♥ K 5
♦ A Q 3 2
♣ 2

East	South	West	North
4 ♥	4 ♠	5 ♥	6 ♠

All Pass

Opening lead: Deuce of hearts

Plan the play.

Solution

North

♠ A 7 6 4 3
♥ None
♦ 7 5 4
♣ A J 7 6 4

West	East
♠ 8 5	♠ None
♥ 10 6 2	♥ A Q J 9 8 7 4 3
♦ K J 6	♦ 10 9 8
♣ Q 10 9 8 5	♣ K 3

South

♠ K Q J 10 9 2
♥ K 5
♦ A Q 3 2
♣ 2

Discard a *diamond* from dummy at trick one. Assuming East wins the ace and returns a diamond, win the ace, draw trumps and discard dummy's remaining diamond on the king of hearts.

If you managed to concoct another line of play for this simple loser-on-loser variation, your imagination needs toning down.

TAKE OFF YOUR SHOES

East-West vul.

Dealer North

North

♠ Q 8 7 6
♥ Q 4
♦ K Q 5
♣ A J 9 2

South

♠ A K J 10 5
♥ J 10
♦ 4 3
♣ K 7 6 5

North	East	South	West
1 ♣	Pass	1 ♠	2 ♥
2 ♠	Pass	4 ♠	All Pass

Opening lead: King of hearts

West continues with the ace of hearts, East playing low-high. At trick three West leads the ten of diamonds to the queen and ace. East returns the jack of diamonds to dummy's king. You draw three rounds of trump ending in dummy, West discarding two hearts, and ruff a diamond in the closed hand West, discarding another heart. How do you play the club suit?

Solution

	North	
	♠ Q 8 7 6 ♥ Q 4 ♦ K Q 5 ♣ A J 9 2	
West		East
♠ 4 ♥ A K 9 8 3 2 ♦ 10 6 ♣ Q 10 4 3		♠ 9 3 2 ♥ 7 6 5 ♦ A J 9 8 7 2 ♣ 8
	South	
	♠ A K J 10 5 ♥ J 10 ♦ 4 3 ♣ K 7 6 5	

West is marked with at least four clubs, as East has turned up with six diamonds, three spades, at least three hearts, so at most one club. The proper play is to lead the king of clubs and a club to dummy's nine. When East shows out, return to your hand with a trump and finesse the jack of clubs. You have now earned the respect of the table. You have counted the hand. Things will never be the same again.

SIMPLICITY

Neither side vulnerable

Dealer South

North

♠ K 10 2
♥ A Q J 10
♦ 10 5 4
♣ A 3 2

South

♠ A 9 8 7 6
♥ None
♦ K 9 8 7
♣ K J 6 5

South	North
1 ♠	2 ♥
2 ♠	4 ♠
Pass	

Opening lead: Queen of diamonds

East wins the ace and returns the deuce. Plan the play.

Solution

North
♠ K 10 2
♥ A Q J 10
♦ 10 5 4
♣ A 3 2

West
♠ Q J 5
♥ K 9 3 2
♦ Q J 6 3
♣ Q 9

East
♠ 4 3
♥ 8 7 6 5 4
♦ A 2
♣ 10 8 7 4

South
♠ A 9 8 7 6
♥ None
♦ K 9 8 7
♣ K J 6 5

Your best chance is to make everything as simple for yourself as possible. It is unlikely that the opening lead was a singleton. With A J 6 3 2, East would probably ducked to insure both communications and two diamond tricks. So play the *king* of diamonds. Even if West does ruff you still have chances. However, if you play low and East is short you are in deep trouble.

Assuming the king of diamonds holds, play the ace-king of spades and the ace-queen of hearts, discarding two diamonds if the queen of hearts is not covered.

Now if spades have divided evenly, the hand is over. West wins the king of hearts, but you have two additional hearts in dummy to park your club losers. You wind up losing a spade, a diamond, and a heart.

THINK POSITIVELY

North-South vulnerable

Dealer South

North

♠ 10 9 3
♥ 7 6 5 4
♦ A 7 6
♣ Q 7 6

South

♠ A K
♥ K J 10 9 8
♦ 8 4 3 2
♣ A K

South	West	North	East
1 ♥	2 ♦	2 ♥	Pass
4 ♥	All Pass		

Opening lead: King of diamonds

You win and lead a heart at trick two, East playing low. Which heart do you play?

Solution

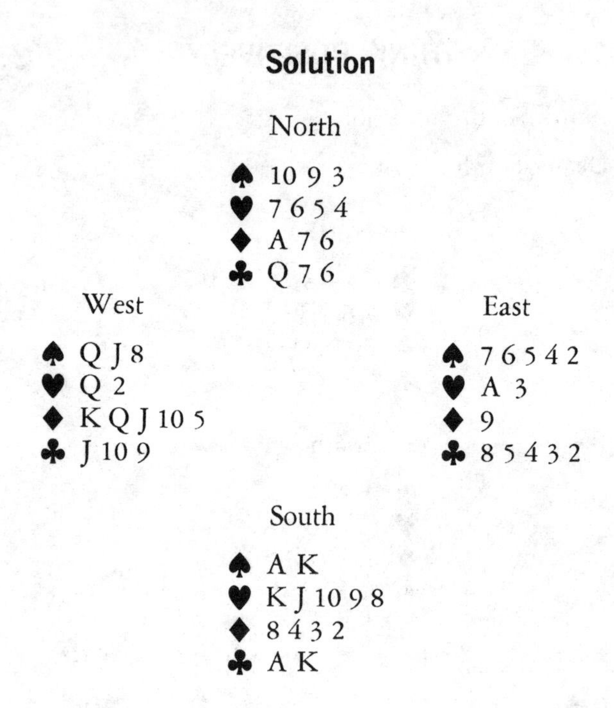

You must play the king for the simple reason that you cannot make the hand if East has the queen of hearts.

Say you play the jack and it forces out the ace. West will simply play three more diamonds, allowing East to overtrump dummy on the last round.

Nor does it do you any good if your jack holds and you find East with A Qx. You still have to lose two hearts and two diamonds.

Therefore your only chance is to find East with either Ax or Axx of trumps, and the proper play beyond any doubt is the *king*.

INSURANCE

Neither side vulnerable
Dealer South

North

♠ 7 6 5 4 3
♥ 8 6
♦ 10 5 4
♣ K Q 10

South

♠ None
♥ K J
♦ A K J 9 8 3
♣ A J 9 8 7

South	West	North	East
1 ♦	Pass	1 ♠	3 ♠
4 ♣	Pass	4 ♦	Pass
5 ♦	All Pass		

Opening lead: Nine of spades

East overtakes with the ten and you ruff. Everyone follows to the ace of diamonds. Now what?

Solution

North

♠ 7 6 5 4 3
♥ 8 6
♦ 10 5 4
♣ K Q 10

West	East
♠ 9 2	♠ A K Q J 10 8
♥ A Q 5 4 3 2	♥ 10 9 7
♦ 7	♦ Q 6 2
♣ 6 5 4 2	♣ 3

South

♠ None
♥ K J
♦ A K J 9 8 3
♣ A J 9 8 7

Enter dummy with a club and lead a diamond to the *jack.* If the finesse wins, the most you can possibly lose is two heart tricks. If the finesse loses you will be able to discard dummy's hearts on your clubs and ruff a heart in dummy.

The only way to lose the hand is to play off two top trumps and then start clubs. East ruffs early and plays a heart, a most unhappy ending for you.

THEY'RE NEVER COLD

North

♠ A Q J 10
♥ A 9 8
♦ A K 7
♣ 10 9 8

South

♠ 2
♥ K Q J 10 3 2
♦ 5 4
♣ A K J 7

Contract 7 ♥

Opening lead: Queen of diamonds

Plan the play

Solution

North

♠ A Q J 10
♥ A 9 8
♦ A K 7
♣ 10 9 8

West

♠ 9 7 5 4
♥ 5 4
♦ Q J 10 6
♣ Q 6 5

East

♠ K 8 6 3
♥ 7 6
♦ 9 8 3 2
♣ 4 3 2

South

♠ 2
♥ K Q J 10 3 2
♦ 5 4
♣ A K J 7

Win the diamond, remove the trumps and play off the ace-king of clubs. If the queen drops it's all over. If it doesn't, lead a spade to the *ace* and run the queen of spades through East. You need to discard two clubs on the spades without losing a trick. If West has the king of spades he must have Kx or Kxx for you to be able to discard two clubs taking the straight spade finesse. However, if you take the ruffing finesse through *East* you get your two club discards regardless of East's spade length.

SAFETY FIRST

North

♠ A 9 7 2
♥ J 4
♦ A K 10 3 2
♣ Q 5

South

♠ J 10
♥ A 7 5 3
♦ J 9 4
♣ A K 9 8

Contract: 3 NT

Opening lead: Three of spades

Can you see any way of insuring nine tricks regardless of the lie of the East-West cards?

Solution

North

♠ A 9 7 2
♥ J 4
♦ A K 10 3 2
♣ Q 5

West	East
♠ 8 6 5 3	♠ K Q 4
♥ Q 8 6	♥ K 10 9 2
♦ 7 6	♦ Q 8 5
♣ J 4 3 2	♣ 10 7 6

South

♠ J 10
♥ A 7 5 3
♦ J 9 4
♣ A K 9 8

The only certain way of insuring nine tricks is to rise with the ace of spades (if you duck, East might shift to an embarrassing heart and the diamond finesse might be off) and play ace and a *low diamond* at tricks two and three.

Playing the low diamond insures four diamond tricks, all you need to make the hand, and guards against a 5-0 diamond split. If you played the ace-king and a low diamond, don't take credit, as a 4-1 diamond division defeats you if the player with the queen of diamonds is stubborn enough to duck the third round of the suit.

Notice that by winning the first spade you do not leave yourself wide open in the suit, as there is no combination of East-West spades that allows them to cash more than three spade tricks when in with the queen of diamonds.

THINK!

North

♠ K 6 3
♥ Q J 9 8
♦ A J 7 6 2
♣ 7

South

♠ 9 4 2
♥ A K 10 7
♦ 5
♣ A Q 6 5 2

Contract: 4 ♥

Opening lead: Queen of spades

You duck the first spade, and when West continues with the ten you duck again, but, alas, to no avail. East simply plays high-low in spades. At trick three West continues with the jack of spades to East's ace. East devilishly returns a trump at trick four. Plan the play.

Solution

North

♠ K 6 3
♥ Q J 9 8
♦ A J 7 6 2
♣ 7

West	East
♠ Q J 10	♠ A 8 7 5
♥ 6 5 4	♥ 3 2
♦ K 10 8 4 3	♦ Q 9
♣ J 8	♣ K 10 9 4 3

South

♠ 9 4 2
♥ A K 10 7
♦ 5
♣ A Q 6 5 2

With a singleton in both hands a crossruff looks best . . . but with the trump switch you can count only nine tricks, seven trump tricks plus two aces. In order to come to ten tricks, win the trump return in dummy and immediately take the *club finesse.* When this works, the ace of clubs is cashed, and the hand played as a straight crossruff.

IT ALWAYS SEEMS LIKE A GUESS

Neither side vulnerable

Dealer West

North

♠ A Q J 2
♥ K J
♦ A J 3 2
♣ 10 7 6

South

♠ 10 9 8 7 6
♥ 10 4 3
♦ K 4
♣ 9 8 2

West	North	East	South
Pass	1 NT	Pass	2 ♠
Pass	3 ♠	All Pass	

Opening lead: King of clubs

Not content to let well enough alone, your loving partner gives you one little boost. Now you have to play at the three level to justify his confidence in you.

West continues with the queen and jack of clubs, East playing the five, four, and three, in that order. At trick four West shifts to the inevitable low heart. Which heart do you play from dummy, and worse, why?

Solution

North

♠ A Q J 2
♥ K J
♦ A J 3 2
♣ 10 7 6

West

♠ K 5 3
♥ Q 6 5 2
♦ 10 6 5
♣ K Q J

East

♠ 4
♥ A 9 8 7
♦ Q 9 8 7
♣ A 5 4 3

South

♠ 10 9 8 7 6
♥ 10 4 3
♦ K 4
♣ 9 8 2

You have to make one assumption before you play any card from the dummy — you must assume the king of spades is onside or else the hand is for practical purposes, unmakeable. Therefore, place the king of spades in the West hand. If that is the case, then East must have the ace of hearts, as West would have opened the bidding had he that card.

Consequently, the proper play from dummy is the *jack* of hearts. You think and play so beautifully.

DETECTIVE WORK

East-West vulnerable

Dealer North

North

♠ K J 3 2
♥ Q 10 8
♦ K Q 7 6
♣ 7 6

South

♠ 7 6
♥ A J 9
♦ A J 10 8 5 4
♣ 10 8

North	East	South	West
Pass	1 ♣	1 ♦	2 ♣
3 ♦	All Pass		

Opening lead: Three of clubs

East wins the king-ace of clubs, West following with the deuce, and exits with a trump, West following. How should you play the spades? (East has one diamond)

Solution

North

♠ K J 3 2
♥ Q 10 8
♦ K Q 7 6
♣ 7 6

West	East
♠ Q 5 4	♠ A 10 9 8
♥ K 7 4	♥ 6 5 3 2
♦ 9 3	♦ 2
♣ Q 9 4 3 2	♣ A K J 5

South

♠ 7 6
♥ A J 9
♦ A J 10 8 5 4
♣ 10 8

Before playing spades, *finesse the queen of hearts.* If the heart finesse loses then East is marked with the ace of spades to justify his opening bid. If East has the king of hearts then West must have the ace of spades to justify his raise. Sometimes the answer to what a player has in one particular suit lies in discovering what he has in another. A word to the wise.

IT'S A LOCK

North

♠ A J 7 6
♥ K J 8
♦ A J 8 2
♣ 7 5

South

♠ K Q 10 9 3
♥ A 10 5
♦ K 4 3
♣ 8 6

Contract: 4 ♠

Opening lead: King of clubs

West cashes the queen of clubs at trick two and shifts to a trump. Trumps are 2-2. Can you spot the sure way of insuring your contract?

Solution

North

♠ A J 7 6
♥ K J 8
♦ A J 8 2
♣ 7 5

West

♠ 4 2
♥ Q 7 6 4
♦ 7 6
♣ K Q J 9 2

East

♠ 8 5
♥ 9 3 2
♦ Q 10 9 5
♣ A 10 4 3

South

♠ K Q 10 9 3
♥ A 10 5
♦ K 4 3
♣ 8 6

You have this one in your hip pocket. Cash the king of diamonds (after drawing the second round of trump) and lead a diamond to the eight spot if West follows with a low diamond. East wins and is endplayed. If West produces the nine or ten of diamonds on the second round of the suit, insert the jack, and once again East is endplayed. The hand is unbeatable because of dummy's eight of diamonds.

PERCENTAGE PLAY

North

♠ 3
♥ 10 8 3 2
♦ Q 4
♣ K J 10 9 6 5

South

♠ A K 7 5
♥ A 4
♦ A K 10 3
♣ A 8 4

South plays 6 ♣ after having opened an artificial 2 ♣. West leads the five of hearts, East plays the king. Plan the play.

Solution

North

♠ 3
♥ 10 8 3 2
♦ Q 4
♣ K J 10 9 6 5

West		East
♠ Q 10 8 4		♠ J 9 6 2
♥ Q 9 5		♥ K J 7 6
♦ 8 7 6		♦ J 9 5 2
♣ Q 3 2		♣ 7

South

♠ A K 7 5
♥ A 4
♣ A K 10 3
♣ A 8 4

Win the heart and play the ace-king of clubs. If the queen drops, relax, it's all over. You are either making six or seven depending upon whether or not the jack of diamonds drops under the ace-king-queen.

If the queen of clubs does not oblige, lead a diamond to the queen and a diamond to the *ten.* This is the percentage play for the four diamond tricks which you need to discard two hearts from dummy, along with your extra good spade which will provide a parking place for the remaining losing heart.

One caution. If the player that has the three clubs, let's say West, turns up with five little diamonds, play your good diamonds before trying to cash two spades. However, with any other distribution play three rounds of diamonds, then two spades and then the fourth diamond. It would be a shame to lose this hand if West started with 1-4-5-3 distribution by trying to cash the spades prematurely when you know for a certainty you can cash the diamonds. (West would ruff the second spade with the queen of clubs and cash a heart.)

IS WEST KIDDING?

North

♠ A Q 3 2
♥ None
♦ 8 6 5 3 2
♣ 8 6 3 2

South

♠ K 10
♥ A K Q
♦ A Q 4
♣ A K 10 9 7

Contract: 6 ♣

Opening lead: Ten of hearts

You discard a diamond from dummy, winning the first heart in your hand. At trick two you play the ace of clubs and West furnishes the queen. How should you continue?

Solution

North
♠ A Q 3 2
♥ None
♦ 8 6 5 3 2
♣ 8 6 3 2

West	East
♠ J 9 8 7	♠ 6 5 4
♥ 10 9 8 7 6	♥ J 5 4 3 2
♦ K J 9	♦ 10 7
♣ Q	♣ J 5 4

South
♠ K 10
♥ A K Q
♦ A Q 4
♣ A K 10 9 7

Cash a second high heart, discarding a second diamond from dummy, ruff a third heart in dummy, and lead a low club to the *ten.* If the club holds you are playing for overtricks. However, if West, the sneak, has the Q J of clubs, his triumph will be short-lived.

Upon winning the club West will be endplayed in three suits. If he returns a diamond, discard your remaining diamond loser on an extra spade winner. If he returns a spade, win the king-ten of spades, and enters dummy with the eight of clubs to discard your two remaining diamonds on the ace-queen of spades. It goes without saying that you have retained the eight of clubs in dummy to provide for this contingency. (If you squandered your eight of clubs earlier, keep it a secret for the rest of your life.)

Finally, if West returns a heart, ruff in dummy, discarding a diamond from your hand, and discard the queen of diamonds on dummy's extra spade winner. Even if the finesse in clubs loses, you win!

JEWELS

Neither side vulnerable

Dealer West

North

♠ A 10
♥ 7 4 2
♦ K 9 7 4 3
♣ J 7 5

South

♠ K J 9 8 4 3
♥ K 6 5
♦ A 2
♣ A 2

West	North	East	South
Pass	Pass	1 ♥	Dbl.
Pass	2 ♦	Pass	2 ♠
Pass	3 ♠	Pass	4 ♠

All Pass

Opening lead: Three of hearts

East wins the ace of hearts and shifts to the king of clubs. Whom do you play for the queen of spades? How do you play the hand?

Solution

North

♠ A 10
♥ 7 4 2
♦ K 9 7 4 3
♣ J 7 5

West	East
♠ Q 7 5	♠ 6 2
♥ J 8 3	♥ A Q 10 9
♦ Q 10 8	♦ J 6 5
♣ 9 6 4 3	♣ K Q 10 8

South

♠ K J 9 8 4 3
♥ K 6 5
♦ A 2
♣ A 2

Don't tell me you let me throw you off with that little bit about the queen of spades! Your best play is to win the club and play ace-king and ruff a diamond with a middle spade.

If diamonds break 3-3, simply play the *king-ace* of spades and discard a loser on dummy's fourth diamond.

If diamonds are 4-2, and East turns up with the length and West fails to overruff your middle spade play East for the queen of spades. Also, if West turns up with the four diamonds play East for the queen of spades because (a) he is the bidder and (b) with his shortness in diamonds he figures to have the spade length. (Obviously East has opened a four card heart suit from the lead and subsequent plays.)

100%

North
♠ 4
♥ A 8 7 5 4
♦ A Q 10 6 4
♣ A 4

South
♠ A 9 6
♥ K Q J 10 9 6
♦ 9 5
♣ 9 5

Contract: 6 ♥

Opening lead: King of spades

You win the ace and play the king of hearts, all following. How do you play to insure this slam against *any* distribution of the adverse cards?

Solution

North

♠ 4
♥ A 8 7 5 4
♦ A Q 10 6 4
♣ A 4

West

♠ K Q J 10 8
♥ 2
♦ 3
♣ Q 10 8 7 3 2

East

♠ 7 5 3 2
♥ 3
♦ K J 8 7 2
♣ K J 6

South

♠ A 9 6
♥ K Q J 10 9 6
♦ 9 5
♣ 9 5

At trick three South leads the *five* of diamonds to the *ace.* Assuming nothing happens, South reenters his hand with a trump and leads the nine of diamonds. If West follows, the hand is assured. Play the queen from dummy. If it loses to the king you have sufficient entries to establish the fifth diamond. If West shows out on the second diamond, run the nine to East's jack, later running the queen through East's marked king to set up the ten for a club discard.

FOR YOUR LIFE

North

♠ A Q 9
♥ A J 8 7 6
♦ Q
♣ Q 4 3 2

South

♠ 10 7 2
♥ K 10 9
♦ A 10 3 2
♣ A K 5

Contract 3 NT

Opening lead: Six of spades

Assume you were playing this contract for your life, how would you play to insure nine tricks?

Solution

	North	
	♠ A Q 9	
	♥ A J 8 7 6	
	♦ Q	
	♣ Q 4 3 2	
West		East
♠ 6 5 4		♠ K J 8 3
♥ 3 2		♥ Q 5 4
♦ K J 5 4		♦ 9 8 7 6
♣ J 8 7 6		♣ 10 9
	South	
	♠ 10 7 2	
	♥ K 10 9	
	♦ A 10 3 2	
	♣ A K 5	

For your life, rise with the ace of spades, lead a heart to the king and run the ten of hearts into East. Assuming this loses you have nine sure tricks, and a tenth if the clubs are 3-3.

If you duck the spade lead or put in the queen, the cards could lie in such a way that you would live to regret your greediness. East could shift to a diamond. True, with the actual lie of the cards you could still come out of this by rising with the ace and finessing the heart into *West*. Even if the finesse fails, the defenders could only take two more diamonds, but then again the diamonds might be placed differently, and you could lose three or even more diamond tricks!

On the other hand, if you duck the diamond switch around to the queen, the cards might be as you see them. West wins and plays a second spade, which you duck again. This time East wins and returns a second diamond, and you feel as if your head is on a swivel. You now find yourself down to guessing the queen of hearts for you contract. Ugh.

OUT OF THIN AIR

Neither side vulnerable

Dealer West

North

♠ 10 4
♥ J 8 3
♦ K 8 5 3
♣ K 9 7 4

South

♠ K 7 3
♥ A K Q 9 7
♦ Q 10
♣ 10 6 2

West	North	East	South
Pass	Pass	2 ♠*	3 ♥
Pass	4 ♥	All Pass	

*Weak Two Bid

Opening lead: Deuce of spades

East wins the ace and returns the queen to your king, and West's five. Now what?

Solution

North
♠ 10 4
♥ J 8 3
♦ K 8 5 3
♣ K 9 7 4

West	East
♠ 6 5 2	♠ A Q J 9 8
♥ 10 6 5 4	♥ 2
♦ A 7 2	♦ J 9 6 4
♣ A J 3	♣ Q 8 5

South
♠ K 7 3
♥ A K Q 9 7
♦ Q 10
♣ 10 6 2

This time you only need to find with East the jack of diamonds and West with the ace of clubs. Not too bad a parlay once East turns up with good spades as he surely cannot have the ace of clubs.

Ruff a spade at trick three and lead a diamond to the *ten.* West does best to win and attack clubs. You win the king, cross to the queen of diamonds and then over to the jack of hearts to discard your losing club on the king of diamonds. You still have a trump in dummy to return to your hand to draw the remaining lurkers (that's what they call small trumps in England) and sit back and wait for West to tell East he should have shifted to clubs earlier.

PLAY TO MAKE

Neither side vulnerable

Dealer East

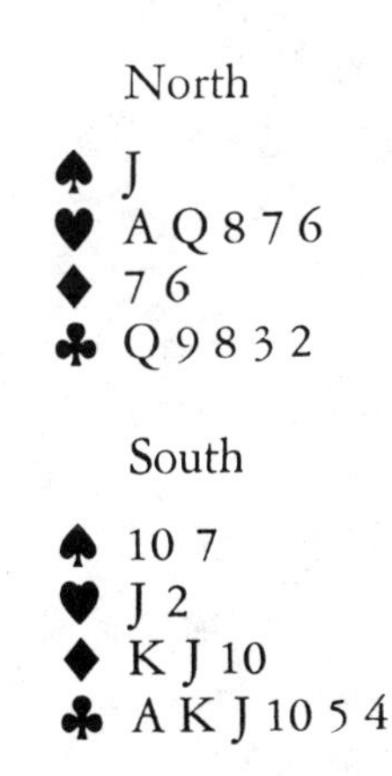

North

♠ J
♥ A Q 8 7 6
♦ 7 6
♣ Q 9 8 3 2

South

♠ 10 7
♥ J 2
♦ K J 10
♣ A K J 10 5 4

East	South	West	North
1 ♠	2 ♣	4 ♠	5 ♣
All Pass			

Opening lead: Three of spades

East wins the king and shifts to a low diamond. Which diamond should you play, and why?

Solution

North

♠ J
♥ A Q 8 7 6
♦ 7 6
♣ Q 9 8 3 2

West	East
♠ Q 8 5 3 2	♠ A K 9 6 4
♥ K 10 4 3	♥ 9 5
♦ Q 8 5 4	♦ A 9 3 2
♣ None	♣ 7 6

South

♠ 10 7
♥ J 2
♦ K J 10
♣ A K J 10 5 4

You should play the king of diamonds. Why? Because you can see East has the ace, silly. No, that's not the reason! In order to make the hand you must assume the king of hearts is onside. If that is the case then East needs the ace of diamonds to justify his opening bid.

There's quite a lesson to be learned from this hand: When you absolutely need one particular card (the king of hearts) to be in one particular hand to make a contract, ASSUME IT IS, and then try to place the other important cards from the bidding.

GOOD DUMMY

Neither side vulnerable

Dealer West

North

♠ Q 2
♥ J 3 2
♦ 7 6 5
♣ J 5 4 3 2

South

♠ A K 10 9 8 7 6
♥ A Q
♦ 3 2
♣ A 10

West	North	East	South
1 ♦	Pass	1 ♥	4 ♠

All Pass

Opening lead: King of diamonds

West continues with the ace and a low diamond to East's queen. Plan the play.

Solution

North

♠ Q 2
♥ J 3 2
♦ 7 6 5
♣ J 5 4 3 2

West	East
♠ 5 3	♠ J 4
♥ K 5	♥ 10 9 8 7 6 4
♦ A K J 9 4	♦ Q 10 8
♣ Q 9 8 7	♣ K 6

South

♠ A K 10 9 8 7 6
♥ A Q
♦ 3 2
♣ A 10

Your best play is to ruff the third round of diamonds and lead the *queen of hearts!* You are actually making a safety play. If you go to the dummy with the queen of spades to take the heart finesse, you will feel rather silly if West has the king, as you have cleverly shut yourself from dummy's jack. On the other hand, if you play the ace first and then the queen, you lose if East has six hearts to the king and leads a third heart while West remains with trump.

Leading the queen works anytime hearts are 5-3 or if West has a doubleton heart with one or two spades.

Follow the play. West wins the king of hearts and shifts to a club. South wins, cashes the ace of spades, the ace of hearts, enters dummy with the queen of spades and disposes of his losing club on the jack of hearts.

DEUCES

North

♠ Q 3 2
♥ 6 5 4 3
♦ 8 7 2
♣ 6 4 2

South

♠ A K J 10
♥ A K 2
♦ A K Q
♣ A K J

You had this hand in a dream one day.
You dreamt you wound up in six no trump.
The opening lead was the jack of diamonds.
What's the best play not to turn your dream into a nightmare?

Solution

North

♠ Q 3 2
♥ 6 5 4 3
♦ 8 7 2
♣ 6 4 2

West	East
♠ 9 7 4	♠ 8 6 5
♥ J 8 7	♥ Q 10 9
♦ J 10 9 4	♦ 6 5 3
♣ Q 9 3	♣ 10 8 7 5

South

♠ A K J 10
♥ A K 2
♦ A K Q
♣ A K J

Lead a low heart at trick two. You can then win any return and cash the ace-king of hearts to see whether or not they break 3-3. If they do, discard your losing club on the fourth heart. If they don't, fall back on the club finesse. If you took the club finesse prematurely or played ace-king and a heart rather than a low heart (this loses if hearts are 4-2 and the club queen is on side) forget about having a good night's sleep. You don't deserve it.

CONFIDENCE BUILDER AND DESTROYER

North

♠ 10 8 5
♥ J 10
♦ A 7 2
♣ K Q J 9 2

South

♠ K Q J 9 7
♥ K Q 6
♦ K 9 4
♣ 6 3

Contract: 4 ♠

Opening lead: Queen of diamonds

Plan the play.

Solution

North

♠ 10 8 5
♥ J 10
♦ A 7 2
♣ K Q J 9 2

West

♠ 6
♥ 8 4 3
♦ Q J 10 5 3
♣ A 10 8 7

East

♠ A 4 3 2
♥ A 9 7 5 2
♦ 8 6
♣ 5 4

South

♠ K Q J 9 7
♥ K Q 6
♦ K 9 4
♣ 6 3

If you had trouble with this one, this may not exactly be the right book for you. This was one to give you confidence! Win the diamond lead in *dummy* and start on hearts. You must try to avoid your diamond loser before the opponents build up a trick in that suit.

Assuming someone wins the ace of hearts and returns a diamond, you win and discard a diamond from dummy on your long heart. Now lead a club *before* you ruff a diamond, just in case someone has 4-5-2-2 distribution and discards a club on the diamond ruff later ruffing a club.

Take half credit if you ruffed a diamond before leading a club. The easy part was supposed to be leading hearts immediately.

A BAD BREAK

North

♠ A 2
♥ A 9 6 5 4
♦ 7 6 5
♣ K Q 2

South

♠ K 4
♥ 3
♦ A Q 9
♣ A J 10 9 8 7 6

Conract: 6 ♣

Opening lead: Jack of spades

You win the king and immediately lead a heart to the ace and ruff a heart, all following. You enter dummy with a trump, both following, and lead a third heart, upon which East discards a spade. Now what?

Solution

North

♠ A 2
♥ A 9 6 5 4
♦ 7 6 5
♣ K Q 2

West	East
♠ J 10 9	♠ Q 8 7 6 5 3
♥ Q 10 8 7 2	♥ K J
♦ K 10 2	♦ J 8 4 3
♣ 4 3	♣ 5

South

♠ K 4
♥ 3
♦ A Q 9
♣ A J 10 9 8 7 6

Actually, things aren't all that bad. Ruff the third heart, enter dummy with a trump, and ruff dummy's next to last heart. Now back to the ace of spades, lead dummy's last heart and discard the nine of diamonds. West is in, and must either lead a diamond or, equally good for you, a spade.

If you even as much as thought of monkeying with the diamonds, don't admit to it in public.

RATING SCALE

125 - 100	DON'T GLOAT YET
95 - 75	SHOWS PROMISE
70 - 50	SHOWS HOPE
45 - 25	SHOWS YOU MISADDED
LESS	SHOWS YOU BOUGHT THE WRONG BOOK.

SO MANY FINESSES

North

♠ A J 10
♥ A K 10 8
♦ A 7 6 5
♣ J 7

South

♠ 9 5 4
♥ Q 3
♦ K 4
♣ A K 10 4 3 2

Contract: 6 ♣

Opening lead: Deuce of spades

Which finesses do you take and which do you give up?

Solution

North

♠ A J 10
♥ A K 10 8
♦ A 7 6 5
♣ J 7

West

♠ Q 8 3 2
♥ J 9 4 2
♦ J 9
♣ Q 9 5

East

♠ K 7 6
♥ 7 6 5
♦ Q 10 8 3 2
♣ 8 6

South

♠ 9 5 4
♥ Q 3
♦ K 4
♣ A K 10 4 3 2

The first step is to win the ace of spades. That's one finesse you can live without. Next the *seven* of clubs is led to the ace just in case there is a singleton queen of clubs lurking around.

Dummy is now entered with a diamond and the jack of clubs is led. This play is made for two reasons. Some players think that it is a sin not to cover an honor with an honor, and a player with Q98x might cover to insure his trump trick. Assuming the jack is not covered, rise with the king. If the queen still hasn't dropped you are now down to your last big play — the queen of hearts followed by a heart to the *ten* in order to dispose of the two spades. Win some — lose some.

PLACING HONORS

East-West vulnerable

Dealer North

North
♠ 7 4 2
♥ A 9 8
♦ K 9 3
♣ A 10 5 4

South

♠ A 10 8
♥ None
♦ A Q 10 8 7 6 2
♣ Q 3 2

North	East	South	West
Pass	Pass	1 ♦	1 ♥
2 NT	3 ♥	4 ♦	Pass
5 ♦	All Pass		

Opening lead: Queen of hearts

Trumps are 2-1, East having a small singleton.

Plan the play.

Solution

North

♠ 7 4 2
♥ A 9 8
♦ K 9 3
♣ A 10 5 4

West	East
♠ K 9 6	♠ Q J 5 3
♥ Q J 10 7 4 2	♥ K 6 5 3
♦ J 5	♦ 4
♣ K 6	♣ J 9 8 7

South

♠ A 10 8
♥ None
♦ A Q 10 8 7 6 2
♣ Q 3 2

West's opening lead marks East with the king of hearts, and West's non-spade lead marks East with some spade honors. Therefore, West should have the king of clubs, no? Yes.

Best play is to ruff the opening lead, draw two trumps ending in your hand, and lead a club to the ten. If this loses to the king you make five or six. Assuming it loses to the jack and a spade comes back, win (or duck and win the spade return and enter dummy with the ace of clubs. If the king falls, that's all she wrote. If it doesn't, the queen of clubs is discarded on the ace of hearts, and a club ruffed in the closed hand gives you one more chance — 3-3 clubs.

Given that West should have the king of clubs, this line of play works anytime West has both the king and jack of clubs, the doubleton king of clubs, or clubs are 3-3. Good enough?

WRONG CONTRACT

North

♠ A 10 3 2
♥ J 9 5
♦ Q J 4
♣ K 10 8

South

♠ K Q J 9
♥ A 4
♦ A 10 9 8
♣ A J 9

You will discuss the bidding after the hand to determine why you are in three no trump instead of four spades, but now you must concern yourself with the matter at hand.

West leads the three of hearts. Hopefully, you play the nine. This is greeted by the ten, which you duck. East continues with the king of hearts, West playing the deuce. Where do you go from here?

Solution

North
♠ A 10 3 2
♥ J 9 5
♦ Q J 4
♣ K 10 8

West	East
♠ 8 6 5	♠ 7 4
♥ Q 8 7 3 2	♥ K 10 6
♦ K 3	♦ 7 6 5 2
♣ 7 6 5	♣ Q 4 3 2

South
♠ K Q J 9
♥ A 4
♦ A 10 9 8
♣ A J 9

First, avoid taking finesses if you don't have to. Finesses never work in quizzes, by the way. You can avoid all finesses and insure your contract providing West has no more than five hearts and less than four spades.

Play the king-queen and nine of spades to dummy's ten, retaining the ace as a later entry. Now the jack of hearts, discarding a diamond. East can take two more hearts, and you discard another diamond and a club, and dummy two diamonds. West must now break from one minor or the other, either play giving you your ninth trick.

DELICACY

North

♠ A K 10 9 7
♥ Q J 8 3
♦ A Q 9
♣ A

South

♠ 6 3
♥ A K 10 2
♦ 3 2
♣ Q 8 6 4 2

Due to a slight bidding misunderstanding and partner's flair for the spectacular you find yourself in the rather optimistic contract of 7 ♥!

West leads a trump and East follows with a low trump. Plan the play.

Solution

North

♠ A K 10 9 7
♥ Q J 8 3
♦ A Q 9
♣ A

West

♠ 8 5
♥ 9 7 4
♦ K 8 6
♣ K J 9 7 5

East

♠ Q J 4 2
♥ 6 5
♦ J 10 7 5 4
♣ 10 3

South

♠ 6 3
♥ A K 10 2
♦ 3 2
♣ Q 8 6 4 2

To say the least you're in a bit of trouble. You are going to need the diamond finesse in any case so you might as well take it early before ruffing spades, as West might be able to discard a diamond on a spade ruff, making it impossible for you to ruff three cards in your hand which you might have to do if spades go 4-2. Phew!

Proper technique is to win the king of hearts, finesse the queen of diamonds, cash the ace and ruff a diamond with the *deuce* of hearts. Now the two top spades followed by a spade ruff with the ace of hearts. If spades break 3-3 (ha-ha) you have the balance by simply drawing trumps. If spades break 4-2, enter dummy with the ace of clubs and ruff another spade with the ten of hearts. Now ruff a club with the eight of hearts, draw the remaining trumps with dummy's queen-jack and take your last spade to make your grand slam. You play so beautifully.

CONSERVATION

North
♠ Q 4
♥ A 4 3
♦ A K Q 8 7 5
♣ 8 4

South
♠ A 10 6 3
♥ K 9 7 6 2
♦ 2
♣ Q 10 5

Contract: 4 ♥

Opening lead: Five of hearts

You seem to have received a fortunate lead. Can you take full advantage? Plan the play.

Solution

North
♠ Q 4
♥ A 4 3
♦ A K Q 8 7 5
♣ 8 4

West
♠ K 9 5
♥ 10 5
♦ J 10 4 3
♣ A J 7 6

East
♠ J 8 7 2
♥ Q J 8
♦ 9 6
♣ K 9 3 2

South
♠ A 10 6 3
♥ K 9 7 6 2
♦ 2
♣ Q 10 5

You must assume trumps are 3-2 unless you enjoy playing for practice. Win the king of hearts, lead a diamond to the ace and ruff a diamond, but *not* with the deuce of hearts. Lead a heart to the ace, but *not* the deuce, and begin to run diamonds until someone ruins your fun by trumping. (You are discarding clubs.) The worst from your point of view is for the third diamond to be ruffed. The opponents can then cash two clubs and play a spade. Assuming it is East that leads the spade, win the ace and enter dummy with your precious deuce of hearts, and discard your remaining three spades on dummy's good diamonds.

This line of play works anytime trumps are 3-2 and diamonds no worse than 4-2. (Note: The way the cards lie you can get home by winning the king of hearts and immediately playing three top diamonds, shedding two clubs as East ruffs high. South now has two additional trump entries to establish the diamonds. This line just happens to work because the player with the long trump has the short diamonds. If the player with the doubleton trump had a doubleton diamond the hand could collapse with this line of play.)

CAUTION

Both vulnerable

Dealer North

North

♠ J
♥ 10 9 4
♦ K Q J 3
♣ A K 10 6 2

South

♠ K Q 10 2
♥ K Q 8 7 6 5
♦ A
♣ 9 5

North	East	South	West
1 ♦	1 ♠	2 ♥	Pass
4 ♥!	Pass	4 NT	Pass
5 ♦	Pass	5 ♥	All Pass

Opening lead: Nine of spades

Your partner's exuberance has put you in a sticky position. East wins the ace of spades and returns a spade, West playing the three. Plan the play.

Solution

North

♠ J
♥ 10 9 4
♦ K Q J 3
♣ A K 10 6 2

West

♠ 9 3
♥ J 3
♦ 10 8 7 6 2
♣ J 8 7 3

East

♠ A 8 7 6 5 4
♥ A 2
♦ 9 5 4
♣ Q 4

South

♠ K Q 10 2
♥ K Q 8 7 6 5
♦ A
♣ 9 5

The danger is that East will win the first heart and lead a third spade, allowing West to make the jack of hearts. There is no recourse if West has Jxx of hearts, but at least you can protect against Jx.

Cash the ace of diamonds at trick three, enter dummy with a club and discard both remaining spades on the diamonds. Now lead a heart. If East rises and returns a spade, ruff high and cash the remaining high heart hoping to drop the jack. This play loses if East has AJx of hearts and is smart enough to play the ace immediately. You can't have everything.

HANG LOOSE

North

♠ 4 2
♥ K J 10 9 8
♦ Q 10
♣ A 10 8 4

South

♥ K J 7 5
♥ A Q 7 6 5
♦ A 4
♣ Q 3

Contract: 4 ♥

Opening lead: Two of hearts

East follows, plan the play.

Solution

North
♠ 4 2
♥ K J 10 9 8
♦ Q 10
♣ A 10 8 4

West	East
♠ Q 10 9 3	♠ A 8 6
♥ 2	♥ 4 3
♦ K 8 6 5 2	♦ J 9 7 3
♣ K 6 2	♣ J 9 7 5

South
♠ K J 7 5
♥ A Q 7 6 5
♦ A 4
♣ Q 3

Win the heart on the table and lead a *low club* at once! If East has the king your problems are over as you will be able to discard a diamond on the ace of clubs.

If the queen loses and a trump comes back, play ace and ruff a club and exit with the ace and a diamond. If West has the king of diamonds and no fourth club he will have to play a spade. If either East or West wins the king of diamonds and plays a fourth club, ruff high, enter dummy with a trump and try to divine the spade position.

However, going back to trick two, if West does not have the last trump and exits with either minor you are in much better shape. Say a club is returned. Win the ace, ruff a club, enter dummy with a trump, ruff another club and then play ace and a diamond. If West has the king he is endplayed.

The same ending occurs if West exits with a diamond after winning the king of clubs. Say you play the ten and capture East's jack. Strip the hand as before and exit with a diamond, avoiding the spade guess.

Playing a club at trick two is superior to playing a spade. It gives you more chances and allows you to make the hand in many instances without having to guess either spades or diamonds.

Also, it is very important *not* to draw the second trump prematurely. You will then be unable to strip the hand completely and leave trump on both sides assuming West returns a minor suit. (It goes without saying that this line of play also works very well if you ruff out the jack of clubs, thus establishing the ten for a diamond discard.)

BLOCKS

North

♠ Q
♥ Q 10 4 3
♦ A 10 6 5 4 3
♣ 3 2

South

♠ A K J 4
♥ A 2
♦ K
♣ A K Q 8 7 6

Contract: 6 NT

Opening lead: Queen of diamonds

Solution

North
♠ Q
♥ Q 10 4 3
♦ A 10 6 5 4 3
♣ 3 2

West	East
♠ 9 7 5 3 2	♠ 10 8 6
♥ K 9 8 6	♥ J 7 5
♦ Q J 9	♦ 8 7 2
♣ 4	♣ J 10 9 5

South
♠ A K J 4
♥ A 2
♦ K
♣ A K Q 8 7 6

This one could get sticky if clubs break 4-1. True, you have 13 tricks if they break 3-2, but what if they don't?

If you play clubs at once, East wins and plays a heart and now you are in an untenable position if West has the king of hearts. The same would be true if West had four clubs and returned a heart. If East had both the king-jack, or if you misguessed, you would lose an ice-cold hand.

The solution is to *duck a club* at trick two. If East wins and returns a heart, win the ace, enter dummy with a spade, discard your heart on the ace of diamonds and reenter your hand with a club, claiming the balance.

The idea is to keep an extra hand entry in case clubs are 4-1. (Those of you who crossed to the queen of spades, discarded a heart on the ace of diamonds and then played clubs hoping that the player with the four clubs did not have a third diamond, were at least thinking, albeit sideways.)

CAREFUL!

East-West vulnerable

Dealer West

North

♠ Q
♥ A
♦ A J 10 8 3
♣ A K 10 9 8 6

South

♠ 6 2
♥ 9 8 5 3
♦ 9 4 2
♣ J 7 4 3

West	North	East	South
1 ♠	2 NT	3 ♠	Pass
4 ♠	4 NT	Pass	5 ♣

All Pass

Opening lead: King of spades

West continues with the ace of spades. (Trumps are 2-1) Plan the play and be specific.

Solution

North

♠ Q
♥ A
♦ A J 10 8 3
♣ A K 10 9 8 6

West

♠ A K J 9 8 4
♥ K 6
♦ K 7 6 5
♣ 2

East

♠ 10 7 5 3
♥ Q J 10 7 4 2
♦ Q
♣ Q 5

South

♠ 6 2
♥ 9 8 5 3
♦ 9 4 2
♣ J 7 4 3

If you didn't ruff the second spade with a *middle trump,* forget the whole thing. You must plan on two trump entries to your hand to take two diamond finesses and the six of clubs is a very valuable card.

After ruffing, play two top trumps and enter your hand with the seven of clubs to lead a *low* diamond, *not the nine,* to dummy's ten. Assuming this loses and a heart comes back, re-enter your hand with the jack of clubs and run the nine of diamonds. You have just protected against West holding four diamonds to one honor by your play in diamonds, and have lost nothing if West has both honors. If East has both diamond honors you can also forget the whole thing, although you probably would have been doubled long ago.

MAYBE YOU'LL GET LUCKY

North

♠ J 10 9 3 2
♥ A Q 9
♦ A 2
♣ A K 8

South

♠ A 8
♥ K J 3 2
♦ K Q
♣ J 10 9 7 6

Contract: 6 NT

Opening lead: Jack of diamonds

Plan the play.

Solution

North

♠ J 10 9 3 2
♥ A Q 9
♦ A 2
♣ A K 8

West

♠ K 7 6 5
♥ 10 4
♦ J 10 9 8 3
♣ 5 4

East

♠ Q 4
♥ 8 7 6 5
♦ 7 6 5 4
♣ Q 3 2

South

♠ A 8
♥ K J 3 2
♦ K Q
♣ J 10 9 7 6

Hopefully, you won the opening lead on the table and led a low spade to your *eight-spot.* If this holds, you can play on clubs, insuring twelve tricks. If the eight loses, win the diamond return, lead the jack of clubs to the ace, and then a spade back to your ace. If the remaining spade honor falls, claim before you make a mistake; if it does not, close your eyes and take the club finesse.

WHAT A DUMMY

North

♠ J 7 3
♥ 7 6 5 4
♦ 8 6
♣ J 7 3 2

South

♠ A 9
♥ A K Q 9 8
♦ A K Q
♣ A Q 4

Contract: 6 H

Opening lead: Jack of hearts

Trumps are 2-2. Plan the play.

Solution

North

♠ J 7 3
♥ 7 6 5 4
♦ 8 6
♣ J 7 3 2

West

♠ 10 8 6 4
♥ J 10
♦ J 9
♣ K 10 9 8 6

East

♠ K Q 5 2
♥ 3 2
♦ 10 7 5 4 3 2
♣ 5

South

♠ A 9
♥ A K Q 9 8
♦ A K Q
♣ A Q 4

Clearly, you must work with your clubs in the hope of establishing a spade discard. Best play is to cash a second trump and play the ace and a *low* club towards dummy's jack. If West has a doubleton king or plays the king, your troubles are over, as you now have a discard for your nine of spades in the form of the jack of clubs. If West and East both follow with low clubs and the jack wins, play a third club and hope the suit breaks 3-3. Remember you can always get to dummy by ruffing a good diamond.)

Finally, if the jack of clubs holds and East shows out, you have one last trick up your sleeve. Play off the three diamonds, discarding a spade from dummy and then ace and a spade. If East is forced to win this trick he will have to concede a ruff-stuff, allowing you to discard your losing queen of clubs while ruffing in dummy.

BEHIND THE EIGHT BALL

North

♠ Q 5
♥ A J 6 5 4
♦ 9 8 3 2
♣ A K

South

♠ A K 6
♥ 10 8
♦ A J 5 4
♣ J 10 6 5

Contract: 3 NT

Opening lead: Four of spades

Plan the play.

Solution

North
♠ Q 5
♥ A J 6 5 4
♦ 9 8 3 2
♣ A K

West	East
♠ J 10 7 4 3	♠ 9 8 2
♥ K 2	♥ Q 9 7 3
♦ Q 10 6	♦ K 7
♣ Q 7 4	♣ 9 8 3 2

South
♠ A K 6
♥ 10 8
♦ A J 5 4
♣ J 10 6 5

Your best shot is to win the lead in dummy and lead a low heart, inserting the *eight-spot* if East plays low. If the eight drives out an honor, you are home. Win the probable spade return and run the ten of hearts. If this loses you have nine tricks, and if the ten holds, enter dummy with a club and play ace and heart, establishing the fifth heart for the ninth trick.

Some other possibilities: West wins the eight of hearts with an honor and returns a club. Win, and lead a low heart to the ten. If this holds, shift your attention to diamonds by ducking two rounds, but save a small diamond as an entry to dummy's ace of hearts.

Finally, if the eight of hearts loses to the nine, you are more or less reduced to a 3-3 heart break or the queen of clubs dropping under the ace-king.

SPOTS

North

♠ 10 9 8 7
♥ 6 5 4
♦ A 10 9 8
♣ Q 9

South

♠ A K Q J
♥ 3 2
♦ K 7 6
♣ K J 3 2

Contract: 4 ♠

Opening lead: Queen of hearts

East signals with the nine of hearts, and West continues with the seven to East's king. East plays the ace of hearts, South ruffs, and West plays the jack.

South plays the ace-king of spades, West plays the three-deuce and East the five-six. How should South continue?

Solution

North
♠ 10 9 8 7
♥ 6 5 4
♦ A 10 9 8
♣ Q 9

West	East
♠ 4 3 2	♠ 6 5
♥ Q J 10 7	♥ A K 9 8
♦ 5 3	♦ Q J 4 2
♣ A 10 5 4	♣ 8 7 6

South
♠ A K Q J
♥ 3 2
♦ K 7 6
♣ K J 3 2

Your best play at this point is to lead a low club and insert dummy's *nine*. You need two diamond discards from dummy, and playing West for the ten of clubs is certainly the best way to try for them.

Assuming the nine holds, the queen of clubs is played. If West wins you have the balance by drawing the last trump and discarding two diamonds from dummy on the clubs.

If West allows the queen of clubs to hold, reenter your hand with a trump and run the king of clubs, discarding a diamond if it is not covered.

The trap is *not* to draw the third trump. If the player with the ace of clubs ducks two rounds, you will be short a hand entry to establish your clubs. Now you will be forced to try to set up diamonds for three tricks which, in this case, wouldn't work very well.

The danger in leaving the third trump at large is that if West has some holding as A10xxx of clubs and *East* the third trump. West could play a third club after winning the second. However, the spots that have fallen in the trump suit make this contingency highly unlikely. Take only half credit if you drew the third trump before leading a club to the nine. It's a cold, cruel world.

WHAT CAN HAPPEN?

North

♠ Q 7 5
♥ K 10 2
♦ K J 8 7
♣ A K 4

South

♠ K 10 8 4 3
♥ A J 9 5
♦ 10 9 6
♣ J

Contract: 4 ♠

Opening lead: Queen of diamonds

You cleverly cover the opening lead, and East wins the ace and returns the three of diamonds, West playing the deuce. How do you continue?

Solution

North
♠ Q 7 5
♥ K 10 2
♦ K J 8 7
♣ A K 4

West
♠ 9 2
♥ Q 8 3
♦ Q 2
♣ 10 7 6 5 3 2

East
♠ A J 6
♥ 7 6 4
♦ A 5 4 3
♣ Q 9 8

South
♠ K 10 8 4 3
♥ A J 9 5
♦ 10 9 6
♣ J

The problem is to avoid the loss of two spade tricks, along with the ever-present danger of the diamond ruff. The trick is to *start spades from the dummy,* rather than from your own hand.

The reason is this: If you lead a spade from your hand to the queen and ace, East will return a diamond, which West will ruff. If West ruffs with a low spade, you are reduced to a spade guess. If, however, you lead a low spade from dummy and East rises with the ace and gives West a diamond ruff, you will have the balance of tricks, as there will be only two spades left in the game.

If West has the ace of spades, you do not lose anything by leading a spade from dummy to your king. West will win, but the defenders will not be able to take more than one more spade trick, unless West started with four spades, a thought too horrible to contemplate.

WHICH ONE?

North

♠ K Q
♥ J 2
♦ K 10 5 4
♣ A Q J 10 3

South

♠ A J 4 3
♥ A K 9 8 7
♦ 7 3
♣ K 2

Contract: 6 NT

Opening lead: Ten of spades

Plan the play.

Solution

North

♠ K Q
♥ J 2
♦ K 10 5 4
♣ A Q J 10 3

West

♠ 10 9 8 7
♥ 10 4 3
♦ A J 6 2
♣ 9 8

East

♠ 6 5 2
♥ Q 6 5
♦ Q 9 8
♣ 7 6 5 4

South

♠ A J 4 3
♥ A K 9 8 7
♦ 7 3
♣ K 2

With nine tricks in the black suits plus the ace-king of hearts for eleven, you need one more trick. You have two chances: (1) lead up to the king of diamonds, which is 50%, or (2) play the jack of hearts, and if covered, reenter dummy with a spade and lead a heart to the nine, a play which requires East to have both the queen and ten of hearts, approximately a 25% chance. Guess what you should do.

OUCH

North

♠ A K 8 7 6
♥ A 9 5 4 3
♦ Q J 4
♣ None

South

♠ 5 3 2
♥ K
♦ A K 7 6 5
♣ K 10 8 2

Contract: 6 ♦

Opening lead: Ace of clubs

Solution

North
♠ A K 8 7 6
♥ A 9 5 4 3
♦ Q J 4
♣ None

West
♠ J
♥ Q 10 8 7
♦ 10 3 2
♣ A J 9 7 6

East
♠ Q 10 9 4
♥ J 6 2
♦ 9 8
♣ Q 5 4 3

South
♠ 5 3 2
♥ K
♦ A K 7 6 5
♣ K 10 8 2

Ruff the club low in dummy, cross to your king of hearts, and play the queen-jack of diamonds.

If diamonds are 4-1, ruff a low heart, discard two hearts on the ace-king of diamonds, and duck a spade. If spades are 3-2 you are still O.K.

If trumps break in a more civilized manner, ruff a heart low at trick four, draw the last trump, discarding a *spade* from the table, enter dummy with a spade, and play the ace of hearts, discarding a club. If everyone follows, ruff a heart, establishing dummy's fifth heart, cash the king of clubs, discarding yet another spade, and take twelve tricks; six diamonds, one club, three hearts and two spades.

If hearts break 5-2, discard a club on the ace of hearts, but abandon that worthless cause and shift your attention to spades. Duck a spade, once again falling back on a 3-2 spade break. If spades are 3-2, you still have twelve tricks; six diamonds, one club, two hearts and three spades.

LOOKS EASY

North

♠ A 9 8 7 4
♥ None
♦ 9 8 7
♣ Q J 9 8 3

South

♠ K J 10
♥ J 5
♦ A K Q 10 5
♣ A K 10

Contract: 7 ♦

Opening lead: Deuce of clubs
Plan the play.

Solution

North

♠ A 9 8 7 4
♥ None
♦ 9 8 7
♣ Q J 9 8 3

West

♠ Q 6 5
♥ K 10 9 8 7
♦ 3
♣ 7 6 4 2

East

♠ 3 2
♥ A Q 6 4 3 2
♦ J 6 4 2
♣ 5

South

♠ K J 10
♥ J 5
♦ A K Q 10 5
♣ A K 10

Win the club ace and play off two rounds of diamonds. If the suit breaks 3-2 (ha-ha) ruff a heart, reenter your hand with the king of spades, draw the last trump and claim.

The only problem arises when East has four diamonds to the jack. In that one case you are forced to guess the location of the queen of spades. It is more or less a guess, so if you hate West more, run the jack of spades, enter dummy with the ace of spades, finesse the diamond and make your grand slam that way.

On the other hand, if it is East you despise, enter dummy with the ace of spades (leading the jack, of course), finesse the diamond, draw the last trump, run the clubs, and finally finesse the ten of spades.

The key play is *not* to ruff a heart prematurely, as you might need dummy's third trump for a trump finesse. Don't worry if you misguessed the spade — that was not the problem.

IS IT A GUESS?

North

♠ K J 10 9
♥ Q J 2
♦ A Q J 10
♣ J 3

South

♠ A Q 2
♥ A 10 4 3
♦ K 5 4
♣ K 10 2

Contract: 6 NT

Opening lead: Eight of spades

You win the nine in dummy and run the queen of hearts, which holds. When you continue with a low heart to the ten, West discards a low diamond. How do you continue? (East has two spades and two diamonds)

Solution

North
♠ K J 10 9
♥ Q J 2
♦ A Q J 10
♣ J 3

West
♠ 8 7 6 2
♥ 5
♦ 9 8 7 6
♣ A 9 8 7

East
♠ 4 3
♥ K 9 8 7 6
♦ 3 2
♣ Q 6 5 4

South
♠ A Q 2
♥ A 10 4 3
♦ K 5 4
♣ K 10 2

It appears that you have to guess the club position to make the hand. You don't! Simply run off your winners in diamonds and spades. On the last winner from dummy, everyone will have four cards:

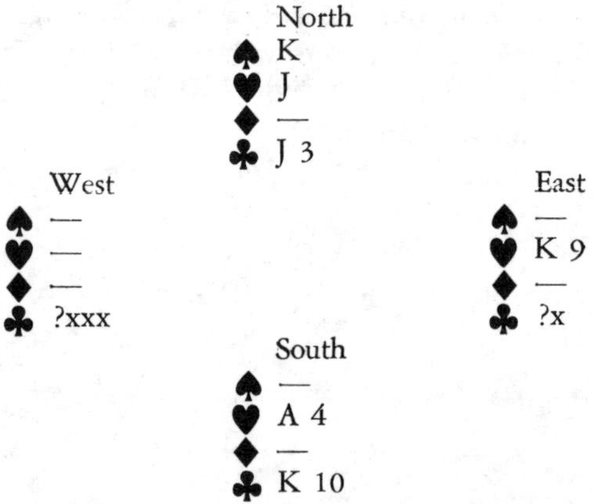

East will be forced to discard a club to retain two hearts, thus reducing his hand to one club. You discard a heart, and West discards a club. When you lead a club from dummy, East's lone honor will appear, and you won't have to guess the suit.

If East produces a low club in this ending, you also won't have to guess the suit—West will be sitting in back of you with the ace-queen and a smile.

HANDLING A RUFF-SLUFF

North-South vulnerable

Dealer East

North

♠ 10 2
♥ 7 4
♦ A J 10 9
♣ K J 10 8 7

South

♠ K Q 8 4 3
♥ 10 8
♦ K Q 7 6
♣ A Q

East	South	West	North
2 ♥*	2 ♠	Pass	3 ♠
Pass	4 ♠	All Pass	

*Weak Two Bid

Opening lead: Deuce of hearts

East wins the first two tricks with the king-ace of hearts, and at trick three plays a third heart, West following with the queen. Plan the play.

Solution

North
♠ 10 2
♥ 7 4
♦ A J 10 9
♣ K J 10 8 7

West	East
♠ A 7 6	♠ J 9 5
♥ Q 3 2	♥ A K J 9 6 5
♦ 8 5 3	♦ 4 2
♣ 9 5 4 2	♣ 6 3

South
♠ K Q 8 4 3
♥ 10 8
♦ K Q 7 6
♣ A Q

Once you realize that West must have the ace of spades (East would hardly open a weak two with A K J of hearts and the ace of spades), there is only one chance — to play East to have J 9x of spades. Ruff the heart return in your own hand, overtake the queen of clubs, and *run the ten of spades* if not covered. If the ten of spades is covered, and your honor loses to the ace, reenter dummy with a diamond, and lead a low spade to the eight-spot. If the ten of spades is covered and one of your honors holds, reenter dummy and lead a spade to the eight spot. If they are going to be stubborn you can be stubborn also.

INHUMANITY

North

♠ A 7 6 4 3
♥ J 3 2
♦ Q 4
♣ K Q 4

South

♠ Q J 5
♥ A K 10 5 4
♦ A K 3
♣ A 3

You arrive at a contract of 6 ♥. West leads the jack of clubs. You win the ace and play the ace of hearts, upon which West deposits a diamond. No matter how long you stare at it, it remains a diamond. Can you see any way of recovering from this diabolical trump division?

Solution

North

♠ A 7 6 4 3
♥ J 3 2
♦ Q 4
♣ K Q 4

West	East
♠ K 10 8	♠ 9 2
♥ None	♥ Q 9 8 7 6
♦ 10 7 6 5 2	♦ J 9 8
♣ J 10 9 8 7	♣ 6 5 2

South

♠ Q J 5
♥ A K 10 5 4
♦ A K 3
♣ A 3

You can recover with the aid of two little miracles. West having the king of spades, and East following politely to your eight side suit winners.

Finesse the spade and cash your eight winners, exiting with a losing spade. If everything goes according to plan, East will have to ruff West's spade trick, and be forced to lead away from his queen of hearts, thus reducing his two natural trump tricks to one.

STICKY, STICKY

North

♠ A 10 9 8
♥ K 6
♦ A K 6 4 3
♣ 9 3

South

♠ Q 5 4
♥ A Q
♦ Q J
♣ A Q J 5 4 2

Contract: 6 NT

Opening lead: Jack of hearts

Where do you win this trick? What do you play at trick two? Plan the play.

Solution

North
♠ A 10 9 8
♥ K 6
♦ A K 6 4 3
♣ 9 3

West		East
♠ K J 7 6		♠ 3 2
♥ J 10 9 3		♥ 8 7 5 4 2
♦ 10 8 7 2		♦ 9 5
♣ 10		♣ K 8 7 6

South
♠ Q 5 4
♥ A Q
♦ Q J
♣ A Q J 5 4 2

Win the first heart with the *ace* and lead the *ace* of clubs. If the ten drops, lead a low club to the nine, and if this holds, back to your hand with a diamond to concede a club to the king.

If the ten of clubs does not fall, simply play a club honor and hope for a pedestrian 3-2 club break. This line of play is better than winning the heart in dummy and taking the club finesse while the diamonds are still blocked. What if West wins the club and plays a spade? Now you don't know what to do, as you have the rest of the tricks if the minor suits break, but you don't if diamonds are 4-2, for example.

Also, what if you finesse the queen of clubs and its holds? West might be holding up. Now what are you going to do? Take the finesse again? Using which entry? It's all too sticky for words.

Notice that the recommended line does not block the diamond suit. (You have two dummy entries, the ace of spades and the king of hearts.) You also see how clubs break, and if they are 4-1 you still have the miniscule hope of picking up three spade tricks if East has the lone jack or West the bare king.

OPTIMISM

Both sides vulnerable
Dealer South

North

♠ A 8 3 2
♥ J 7 3
♦ Q 2
♣ K 7 6 5

South

♠ K J
♥ A K 2
♦ A J 10 9 8
♣ A 8 2

South	North
2 NT (20-22)	4 NT!
6 NT	Pass

Opening lead: Ten of hearts

You must have impressed your partner on a previous hand, as he is a bit short for his quantitative raise. Nevertheless, the rules say that you must play the hand.

At trick one you play the jack from dummy and close your eyes. When you open them, you see that East has followed suit with the four.

This might be your once-a-year-day Where do you go from here?

Solution

North
♠ A 8 3 2
♥ J 7 3
♦ Q 2
♣ K 7 6 5

West		East
♠ 10 6 5		♠ Q 9 7 4
♥ Q 10 9 8		♥ 6 5 4
♦ K 4 3		♦ 7 6 5
♣ 10 4 3		♣ Q J 9

South
♠ K J
♥ A K 2
♦ A J 10 9 8
♣ A 8 2

The best plan available is to lead a low *spade* to the jack. If this holds, cash your king of spades and give up a diamond for twelve tricks.

If the spade finesse loses, you still make the hand if East has no more than three diamonds headed by the king, or makes the mistake of covering the queen with four diamonds to the king. (Of course, you must unblock the king of spades before entering dummy with the king of clubs to take the diamond finesse. It would also be nice if you discard a club on the ace of spades before taking the diamond finesse.)

If you made the mistake of leading the queen of diamonds at trick two, you didn't give yourself much of a chance. If the queen loses, you are reduced, for lack of dummy entries, to a rather remote black suit squeeze. Even a lowly spade finesse is better than that.

A LITTLE SHAKY

North

♠ 7 3 2
♥ 8 6
♦ 7 4
♣ A K 6 5 3 2

South

♠ J 10 4
♥ A K 5 2
♦ A K Q 5
♣ J 10

On the strength of your black suit stoppers you open one no trump. Partner raises to three no trump.

Opening lead: Jack of diamonds, East plays the deuce. Plan the play.

Solution

North

♠ 7 3 2
♥ 8 6
♦ 7 4
♣ A K 6 5 3 2

West

♠ K Q 8
♥ J 9 4
♦ J 10 9 8
♣ Q 8 7

East

♠ A 9 6 5
♥ Q 10 7 3
♦ 6 3 2
♣ 9 4

South

♠ J 10 4
♥ A K 5 2
♦ A K Q 5
♣ J 10

All you have to do to get top marks on this one is to lead the *ten* of clubs at trick two. Why not the jack? Well, when you want an honor covered, lead the higher or highest honor you have, when you don't, lead the lower or lowest.

In this case you do *not* want the club covered as the suit is blocked off if West covers and you will be forced to allow the queen to hold. If West finds the spade shift, that's all she wrote. However, West may not be quite as inclined to cover the ten as the jack, although he should cover the ten with that entryless dummy staring him in the face.

However, if you never give your opponents a chance to go wrong they never will.

FREE FINESSE?

North

♠ 2
♥ 10 9 8 7
♦ K Q 8 7 6
♣ A Q 5

South

♠ A K Q J 10 8 7 4
♥ A K J 2
♦ A
♣ None

After North opens one diamond, South has to restrain himself from bidding eight. The final contract, however, is a conservative seven spades. West leads the deuce of clubs. Plan the play.

Solution

North

♠ 2
♥ 10 9 8 7
♦ K Q 8 7 6
♣ A Q 5

West	East
♠ 9 6 5	♠ 3
♥ Q 6 5	♥ 4 3
♦ J 9 5	♦ 10 4 3 2
♣ J 9 4 2	♣ K 10 8 7 6 3

South

♠ A K Q J 10 8 7 4
♥ A K J 2
♦ A
♣ None

You shouldn't have any trouble with this old cutie. Simply discard the ace of diamonds on the ace of clubs (look at your partner's face for signs of terror and/or admiration) and then discard two hearts on the king-queen of diamonds. After the expected standing ovation, claim the balance.

A pox on you if you played dummy's queen of clubs at trick one. You have just mangled a grand slam!

EIGHT EVER NINE NEVER

North

♠ 6 5 3
♥ Q 4
♦ A 10 5 4
♣ K Q 3 2

South

♠ K Q 2
♥ A 6 3
♦ K J 9 8 7
♣ A 4

Contract: 3 NT

Opening lead: Jack of clubs

Plan the play.

Solution

North
♠ 6 5 3
♥ Q 4
♦ A 10 5 4
♣ K Q 3 2

West	East
♠ J 7 4	♠ A 10 9 8
♥ J 10 5	♥ K 9 8 7 2
♦ Q 6 2	♦ 3
♣ J 10 9 8	♣ 7 6 5

South
♠ K Q 2
♥ A 6 3
♦ K J 9 8 7
♣ A 4

Don't tell me you believe in nursery rhymes! This hand is ice-cold if you can simply collect four diamond tricks without having your heart stopper attacked by West.

Simply win the club in your hand, cash the king of diamonds and run the nine of diamonds through West. If the finesse loses, you can always build up at least one spade trick before anybody can do anything to you in hearts.

Notice that if you still believe in poetry and play off your two top diamonds, West, upon winning his queen, can shift to the jack of hearts and defeat your laydown three no trump. What a shame — but you're to blame.

RATING SCALE

125 - 100	LAUDABLE
95 - 75	CREDITABLE
70 - 50	PASSABLE
45 - 25	MISERABLE
LESS	UNPRINTABLE

TECHNIQUE

Both sides vulnerable

Dealer North

North

♠ K J 3
♥ K 4 3
♦ J 7 6
♣ A K 10 6

South

♠ A Q 10 8 7 6
♥ Q 5 2
♦ A Q 5
♣ Q

North	South
1 NT	3 ♠
4 ♠	4 NT
5 ♦	6 ♠
Pass	

Opening lead: Deuce of spades
Spades are 2-2. Plan the play.

Solution

North
♠ K J 3
♥ K 4 3
♦ J 7 6
♣ A K 10 6

West	East
♠ 9 2	♠ 5 4
♥ 9 8 6	♥ A J 10 7
♦ K 10 4	♦ 9 8 3 2
♣ 9 7 5 3 2	♣ J 8 4

South
♠ A Q 10 8 7 6
♥ Q 5 2
♦ A Q 5
♣ Q

At first glance, it appears that if you can guess the location of the heart ace and lead through the player with that card, and the heart ace is ducked, your two remaining hearts can be discarded on clubs, and a diamond conceded if necessary. (If the ace of hearts is taken before you spend a heart honor, you can discard two diamonds on the clubs and make the slam that way.)

Unfortunately, this is only half true. If you cash your queen of clubs (after drawing a second round of trumps) and lead a low heart towards dummy, bad things could happen.

If East has the ace of hearts, he captures dummy's king and returns a diamond. You haven't been able to test the clubs to see whether or not the jack drops, so you have to make a premature decision in diamonds.

If, however, you lead the heart *from dummy* towards your hand, you are in much better shape. If East has the ace of hearts, the hand is immediately cold, and if West has the ace, you will have a chance to test clubs before taking the diamond finesse.

WHERE THERE'S A WILL

Neither side vulnerable

Dealer East

North
♠ A Q J
♥ J 10 3
♦ J 10 4
♣ A Q 3 2

South
♠ K 10 6 5
♥ K 5
♦ K Q 9 8 7
♣ K 4

East	South	West	North
1 ♥	Dbl.	Pass	2 ♥
Dbl.	3 ♦	Pass	3 ♥
Pass	3 NT	All Pass	

Opening lead: Nine of hearts

You play the ten of hearts from dummy and East contributes the eight. How do you continue?

Solution

North

♠ A Q J
♥ J 10 3
♦ J 10 4
♣ A Q 3 2

West

♠ 9 8 7 3 2
♥ 9 2
♦ 5 3 2
♣ 9 7 6

East

♠ 4
♥ A Q 8 7 6 4
♦ A 6
♣ J 10 8 5

South

♠ K 10 6 5
♥ K 5
♦ K Q 9 8 7
♣ K 4

You could try to steal the contract by "faking a finesse" in diamonds by leading the jack from dummy at trick two. However a strong East would not let you get away with such skulduggery, and you would wind up down two on a cold hand!

You see, there is a legitimate play for the contract if East has at least four clubs. Simply run four rounds of spades, discarding a heart or a diamond from the table. East has two easy discards, a diamond and a heart, but the fourth spade squeezes him in three suits!

If he gives up a club, the clubs run, and if he gives up a second heart, you can knock out the ace of diamonds safely, as East only has three hearts to cash, and the contract is assured.

CONFUSING

North

♠ A K 9 3 2
♥ K 4
♦ A Q J 10
♣ 6 3

South

♠ J 4
♥ A 7 6 3
♦ K 7 6
♣ A Q 9 2

Contract: 6 NT (Your partner has overbid . . . again.)

Opening lead: Three of diamonds, East plays the five. What is your plan of attack?

Solution

North

♠ A K 9 3 2
♥ K 4
♦ A Q J 10
♣ 6 3

West	East
♠ Q 10 6	♠ 8 7 5
♥ J 9 8	♥ Q 10 5 2
♦ 9 8 4 3 2	♦ 5
♣ K J	♣ 10 8 7 5 4

South

♠ J 4
♥ A 7 6 3
♦ K 7 6
♣ A Q 9 2

The best play is to win the diamond in dummy and take the *club finesse.* If the finesse loses, you must play for five spade tricks by leading the jack and later finessing the nine, in effect playing West for Q 10x.

However, if the club finesse wins, you only need four spade tricks, in which case the best play is to lead a low spade towards the jack. If that loses to the queen, play the ace-king and hope the ten drops.

The point of the hand is to play clubs first to see if you need miracles in spades (five tricks) or just a bit of good fortune (four tricks).

NINE OH NINE

North
♠ A Q 7 6 5
♥ J 2
♦ 10 5 3
♣ Q 5 3

South
♠ 2
♥ A K 6
♦ K 8 4 2
♣ A K J 10 9

Contract: 3 NT

West leads the four of hearts, the unbid suit, dummy plays the jack, East the queen and you the king. Now what?

Solution

North

♠ A Q 7 6 5
♥ J 2
♦ 10 5 3
♣ Q 5 3

West	East
♠ 10 4 3	♠ K J 9 8
♥ 10 8 7 4 3	♥ Q 9 5
♦ Q 9 7	♦ A J 6
♣ 4 2	♣ 8 7 6

South

♠ 2
♥ A K 6
♦ K 8 4 2
♣ A K J 10 9

You must try for a ninth trick by either leading up to the king of diamonds or taking the spade finesse. If you take the spade finesse and that loses, the defenders might be able to arrange to defeat you by first continuing with a heart, forcing you to duck, and then switching back to spades. It could happen that the ace of diamonds was well placed with East, but you go set because East would own the setting tricks in spades.

However, if you enter dummy with a club and lead a *diamond* first you have two chances: (1) the ace of diamonds with East; (2) the king of spades with West.

LOOKING AHEAD

East-West vulnerable

Dealer West

North

♠ Q 3
♥ A K 10 8
♦ K 4
♣ K Q 9 5 3

South

♠ A 7 2
♥ 9 7 5 3 2
♦ 10 3
♣ A 8 4

West	North	East	South
Pass	1 ♣	Pass	1 ♥
Pass	3 ♥	Pass	4 ♥
All Pass			

Opening lead: Jack of spades

Hopefully, you play the queen. No luck, East produces the king. Plan the play.

Solution

North

♠ Q 3
♥ A K 10 8
♦ K 4
♣ K Q 9 5 3

West

♠ J 10 9 6
♥ Q J 4
♦ J 9 7 6
♣ J 6

East

♠ K 8 5 4
♥ 6
♦ A Q 8 5 2
♣ 10 7 2

South

♠ A 7 2
♥ 9 7 5 3 2
♦ 10 3
♣ A 8 4

The idea here is never to let West in for a possible diamond lead through the king. This can be done by (1) *ducking* the king of spades, and (2) taking a *first round finesse in hearts.*

Assume East returns a spade. You win the ace and lead a heart to the *ten.* Even if this loses, there are only two more trumps at large and, given a normal club division, you should have no further trouble.

Take no credit if you played one high heart from dummy instead of finessing the ten immediately. Naughty, naughty.

NO WAY OUT

East-West vulnerable

Dealer West

North

♠ A K 6 3
♥ J 9 4
♦ A 7 5
♣ Q 6 2

South

♠ Q J 10 7 4
♥ 10 8 3 2
♦ Q 8
♣ K 5

West	North	East	South
1 ♥	Pass	Pass	1 ♠
Dbl.	Rdbl.	2 ♣	Pass
Pass	3 ♠	All Pass	

Opening lead: King of hearts

West continues with the queen and ace of hearts, East following to the first heart, but shedding two small clubs on the second and third. At trick four, West continues with a low heart, which you ruff high in dummy, East discarding a low diamond this time. It's your ball now.

Solution

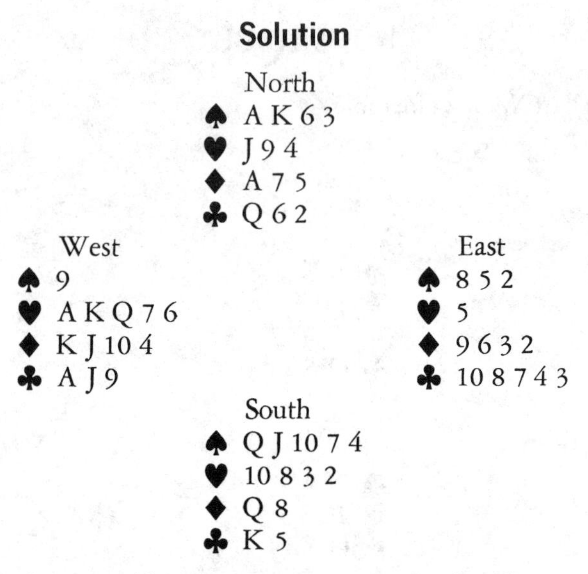

The only reasonable play is to enter your hand with a trump and lead a *low club* toward the queen. West, who is marked with all of the missing high cards, must duck to prevent you from winning two club tricks. After the queen holds, draw four more rounds of trump, reducing all hands to three clubs. This will be the forced ending:

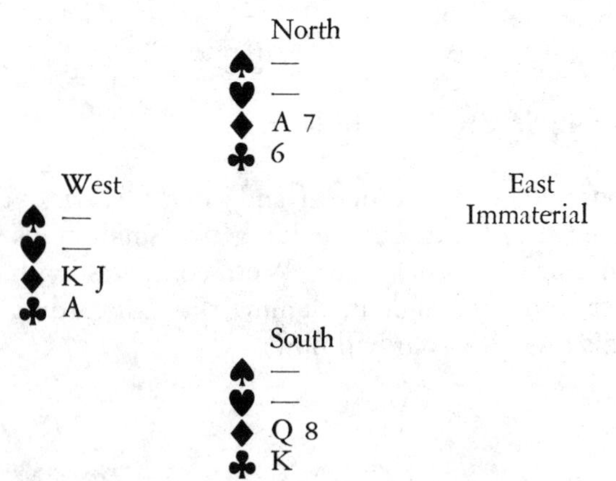

A club is conceded to West and you take the last two tricks. Notice that the hand could have been defeated had East trumped the third round of hearts and returned a diamond — a play found at the table by former world champion Robert Hamman.

FINE CONTRACT

North-South vulnerable

Dealer North

North

♠ K 5
♥ A J 9 3
♦ 10 7
♣ K J 10 7 6

South

♠ A Q 9 8 7 6 4
♥ 10
♦ A K Q 9
♣ 9

North	East	South	West
1 ♣	Pass	2 ♠	Pass
3 ♣	Pass	3 ♠	Pass
4 ♠	Pass	4 NT	Pass
5 ♦	Pass	6 ♠	All Pass

Opening lead: King of hearts

You win in dummy, East playing the four. How do you continue?

Solution

North

♠ K 5
♥ A J 9 3
♦ 10 7
♣ K J 10 7 6

West	East
♠ 10	♠ J 3 2
♥ K Q 8 7 2	♥ 6 5 4
♦ J 8 4 3 2	♦ 6 5
♣ 8 5	♣ A Q 4 3 2

South

♠ A Q 9 8 7 6 4
♥ 10
♦ A K Q 9
♣ 9

Sometimes good players look for intricacies on simple hands. You should simply run the jack of hearts and discard a club. Ruff the probable club return, enter dummy with the king of spades, and discard your nine of diamonds on dummy's nine of hearts. If East ruffs the third round of hearts, overruff, and try to ruff the nine of diamonds in dummy.

You would be surprised how some "geniuses" have tried to make a difficult proposition out of this standard loser on loser position.

A BEAUTIFUL HAND

Both sides vulnerable

Dealer South

North
♠ A 10 7 4 3
♥ A K 4 3
♦ 2
♣ Q 9 6

South
♠ 5
♥ 7 2
♦ A K 9 7 6 3
♣ A K J 10

South	West	North	East
1 ♦	Pass	1 ♠	Pass
2 ♣	Pass	2 ♥	Pass
3 ♦	Pass	4 ♣	Pass
4 NT	Pass	5 ♥	Pass
6 ♣	All Pass		

Opening lead: Queen of hearts

The bidding might not be textbook quality, but the contract is superb. What is your best chance?

Solution

North

♠ A 10 7 4 3
♥ A K 4 3
♦ 2
♣ Q 9 6

West

♠ J 9
♥ Q J 10 8 5
♦ Q 10 8 4
♣ 7 3

East

♠ K Q 8 6 2
♥ 9 6
♦ J 5
♣ 8 5 4 2

South

♠ 5
♥ 7 2
♦ A K 9 7 6 3
♣ A K J 10

You have a chance now that West did not lead a trump to make a truly beautiful play — win the heart (no that's not it, silly) and *duck a diamond!* This unusual safety play insures the contract against a 4-2 division in both minors.

Any major suit return can be won in dummy, your hand entered with a trump, a low diamond ruffed, dummy's last trump overtaken, the remaining trumps drawn, and now the diamonds are all good.

This line of play is superior to a crossruff, as a crossruff requires scoring dummy's six of clubs, which could be troublesome if East has two diamonds

Ducking a diamond is also better than playing the ace-king of diamonds and then discarding from dummy on a third round of diamonds. On the actual layout, East would be able to discard his remaining heart on the third diamond, and then ruff the heart return.

WHAT IF?

Both sides vulnerable

Dealer South

North

♠ A 10 9 6 5
♥ 9 4 3
♦ K 9 8 4 2
♣ None

South

♠ 4 3
♥ A Q 2
♦ A 6 3
♣ A K Q 9 4

South	West	North	East
1 ♣	Pass	1 ♠	Pass
2 NT	Pass	3 ♦	Pass
3 NT	All Pass		

Opening lead: Six of hearts

♥East puts up the ten and you win the queen. Where do you go from here?

Solution

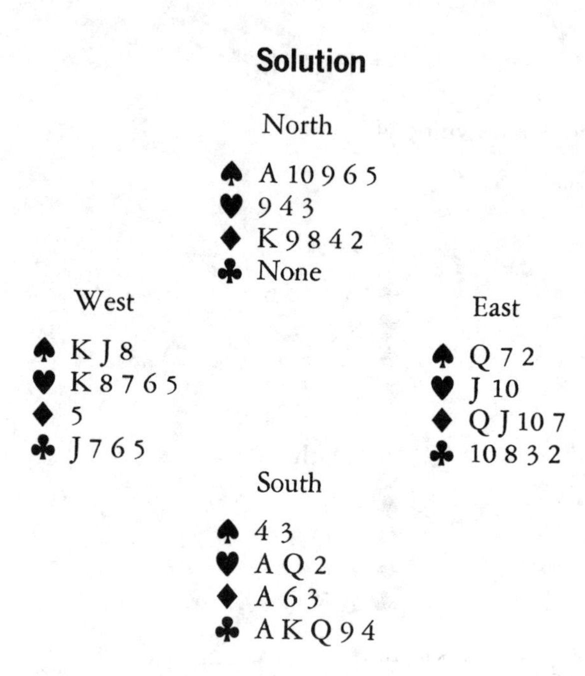

Your best play by far is to lead a *low* diamond to the king and a diamond back to the ace at tricks two and three. If diamonds behave reasonably (3-2), simply concede a diamond. You are now playing for exercise.

However, if diamonds are 4-1, you must shift your attention to clubs. You can either duck a club (best) or play out the three top clubs and concede a club, hoping for a 4-4 division or J 10x in one hand.

Leading the ace of diamonds at trick two in an effort to guard against a singleton honor in the East hand is the correct way to play diamonds but, alas, the wrong way to play the hand. You would then be short the two hand entries necessary to develop the clubs in case of an obscene diamond division.

SHAKY SLAM

North-South vulnerable

Dealer West

North

♠ Q 8 2
♥ K 9 8 7 3
♦ K J 9 2
♣ J

South

♠ A J 9 7 6 5
♥ Q 2
♦ None
♣ A K Q 10 5

West	North	East	South
Pass	Pass	Pass	1 ♠
Pass	2 ♥	Pass	3 ♣
Pass	3 ♠	Pass	4 ♣
Pass	4 ♠	Pass	5 ♦
Pass	6 ♠	All Pass	

Opening lead: Five of diamonds

The idea on this hand is to play the slam better than you and your partner have bid it.

You insert the jack of diamonds at trick one and this fetches the queen, which you ruff. Now what?

Solution

North

♠ Q 8 2
♥ K 9 8 7 3
♦ K J 9 2
♣ J

West		East
♠ K		♠ 10 4 3
♥ J 6 4		♥ A 10 5
♦ 10 8 6 5 3		♦ A Q 7 4
♣ 8 6 4 3		♣ 9 7 2

South

♠ A J 9 7 6 5
♥ Q 2
♦ None
♣ A K Q 10 5

From the lead and play to the first trick, it appears that East has both the ace and queen of diamonds. If East also has the ace of hearts West must have the king of spades, as East failed to open the bidding.

The proper play, therefore, is to smoke out the ace of hearts *before* playing spades. A low heart is led at trick two. If East wins the king of hearts, you have no alternative but to bang down the ace of spades, hoping to snare a stiff king in the West hand.

If, on the other hand, West has the ace of hearts, make the normal play in spades — low to the jack.

INFERENCE

Neither side vulnerable

Dealer East

North

♠ A 10 3 2
♥ 5 4
♦ 8
♣ J 9 8 5 4 3

South

♠ 5
♥ K J 9 8 7 6 2
♦ Q 7 6 2
♣ 7

East	South	West	North
1 ♠	Pass	2 ♣	Pass
2 NT	3 ♥	Dbl.	All Pass

Opening lead: King of clubs

East plays the six at trick one, as you follow. West then shifts to the three of hearts. East wins the ace and returns the ten. If you can work out the heart position you can take seven tricks but if you can't you wind up with six.

Which card do you play from your hand at this point, and why?

Solution

North

♠ A 10 3 2
♥ 5 4
♦ 8
♣ J 9 8 5 4 3

West

♠ J 6 4
♥ Q 3
♦ K J 9 3
♣ A K 10 2

East

♠ K Q 9 8 7
♥ A 10
♦ A 10 5 4
♣ Q 6

South

♠ 5
♥ K J 9 8 7 6 2
♦ Q 7 6 2
♣ 7

You should play the king because: (1) spades must be divided 5-3, as West would not double if he had four card spade support and East would rebid a six card spade suit in preference to rebidding two no trump. (2) Diamonds must be 4-4. (If East had five diamonds he would have rebid them over two clubs and if West had five diamonds his original response would have been two diamonds.)

Once this is conceded, West can have one of two possible distributions: 3-1-4-5 or 3-2-4-4. With the first he would be unlikely to double three hearts, and East would be equally unlikely to rebid two no trump with a singleton club. All signs point to a 2-2 heart distribution. Put that *king* right up there!

A STINKER

Both sides vulnerable

Dealer North

North

♠ A 10 2
♥ A J 9 4 3
♦ K Q
♣ 10 8 7

South

♠ 4
♥ 5
♦ A 8 7 6 5 4
♣ K Q J 9 6

North	East	South	West
1 ♥	Pass	2 ♦	2 ♥ *
Pass	4 ♠	5 ♣	Dbl.
Rdbl.	All Pass		

* Takeout for unbid suits

Opening lead: King of spades

Your partner is showing unheard-of confidence in your bidding, to say nothing of your play. Trying to justify his admiration, you win the opening lead and lead a club to the king which holds. You counter with the king-queen of diamonds. East discards a high heart on the second diamond. Plan the play.

Solution

North
♠ A 10 2
♥ A J 9 4 3
♦ K Q
♣ 10 8 7

West
♠ K Q 8 7 6
♥ None
♦ J 10 3 2
♣ A 4 3 2

East
♠ J 9 5 3
♥ K Q 10 8 7 6 2
♦ 9
♣ 5

South
♠ 4
♥ 5
♦ A 8 7 6 5 4
♣ K Q J 9 6

To judge from what you have seen and heard, West should have the remaining trumps to go along with his known four diamonds. If this is true, West is void in hearts!

Ruff a spade and play the ace and ruff a diamond. Now ruff dummy's last spade and begin to play diamonds through West. This will be the position:

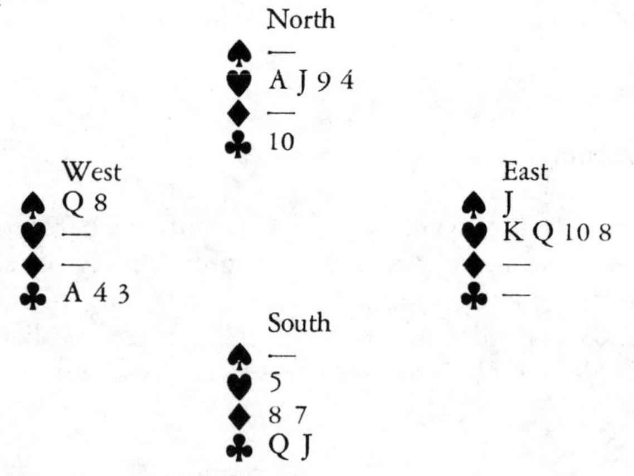

No matter how West plays, he can get no more than two tricks. The key to the hand is not to cash the heart ace prematurely. You can never take more than eleven tricks with or without the heart ace, so why risk a void in the West hand until trick ten?

KING-JACK MISSING

Both sides vulnerable

Dealer West

North

♠ A 4 3 2
♥ Q 8 5
♦ A 10 9 5
♣ K 4

South

♠ Q 5
♥ K J 10 9 7 6
♦ Q 8 7 6
♣ 3

West	North	East	South
Pass	1 ♦	Pass	1 ♥
2 ♣	2 ♥	3 ♣	4 ♥
All Pass			

Opening lead: Ace of clubs

East drops the queen and West shifts to the ten of spades. You win the ace, discard a spade on the king of clubs, and ruff a spade in the closed hand, East producing the jack.

Your king of hearts goes to West's ace, and he leads the nine of spades, which you ruff. You draw a second round of trump ending in dummy, all following, and ruff a spade, West discarding a club.

Now you simply have to play that diamond suit for one loser, how do you do it?

Solution

North

♠ A 4 3 2
♥ Q 8 5
♦ A 10 9 5
♣ K 4

West

♠ 10 9 8
♥ A 3
♦ 3 2
♣ A J 10 8 7 6

East

♠ K J 7 6
♥ 4 2
♦ K J 4
♣ Q 9 5 2

South

♠ Q 5
♥ K J 10 9 7 6
♦ Q 8 7 6
♣ 3

A simple hand. East is marked with the king of diamonds. If West had that card he would have opened the bidding. Furthermore, if West had a singleton diamond along with the ace of trumps, his most likely lead would be a diamond in the hope, perhaps, of putting his partner in with a club for a diamond ruff. Therefore, West figures to have exactly two diamonds. (He should have six clubs for his vulnerable overcall.)

Therefore, abandon the percentage play in diamonds (taking two finesses through East) in favor of playing the *ace and low to the queen*. If West then produces the king of diamonds, quit the game, as it's too tough for someone who thinks as logically as you.

MANAGEMENT

Neither side vulnerable

Dealer South

North

♠ None
♥ 10 5 4
♦ A K J 7 6 5 4
♣ A 5 4

South

♠ Q J 8 7 6 5
♥ A K Q J 2
♦ 2
♣ 7

South	West	North	East
1 ♠	Pass	2 ♦	Pass
2 ♥	Pass	3 ♣	Pass
3 ♥	Pass	5 ♥	Pass
6 ♥	All Pass		

Opening lead: Queen of clubs

How do you manage your red suits to give yourself the best possible chance to land this 25 point slam?

Solution

North

♠ None
♥ 10 5 4
♦ A K J 7 6 5 4
♣ A 5 4

West	East
♠ A 9	♠ K 10 4 3 2
♥ 9 7 6 3	♥ 8
♦ Q 10 3	♦ 9 8
♣ Q J 10 3	♣ K 9 8 6 2

South

♠ Q J 8 7 6 5
♥ A K Q J 2
♦ 2
♣ 7

Your first move after winning the opening lead is to play off the ace-king of trumps. If trumps turn out to be 3-2, play the ace of diamonds. If no queen drops, play the king of diamonds. If the queen drops, draw the last trump with dummy's ten and make seven.

If the queen of diamonds does not drop, ruff a diamond high, and enter dummy with the ten of hearts to make only six. (This is a not a hand to worry about a 4-1 diamond division. You're dead if that happens.)

Finally, if trumps turn out to be 4-1 you must draw the remaining trumps and lead a diamond to the *jack.* If this loses, you can console yourself with two facts: (1) you are not vulnerable, and (2) you played the hand properly no matter what your partner thinks.

DREAM HAND

North

♠ 9 8
♥ 7 5 4
♦ Q 9 8 6 5
♣ K 4 3

South

♠ A K Q J 4 3
♥ A K 9 3
♦ A 7
♣ A

Not one to let a good hand go to your head you restrain yourself from bidding seven and land in six spades with no opposition bidding. West leads the deuce of hearts and East plays the jack. What is your best chance?

Solution

North

♠ 9 8
♥ 7 5 4
♦ Q 9 8 6 5
♣ K 4 3

West

♠ 10 7 5
♥ Q 10 6 2
♦ K J 10
♣ J 9 7

East

♠ 6 2
♥ J 8
♦ 4 3 2
♣ Q 10 8 6 5 2

South

♠ A K Q J 4 3
♥ A K 9 3
♦ A 7
♣ A

Your main chance is to hope (pray) that the hand with four hearts also has the ten of spades so that you can trump your fourth heart in dummy and discard your losing diamond on the king of clubs.

The way to do this is to win the opening lead, cash the ace of clubs, play a second high heart, and exit with a third. If the suit breaks 3-3, you simply must hope that the player who wins this trick has both the ten of spades and the king of diamonds making it impossible for him to exit safely.

If, however, the cards are as they appear in the diagram the defense is helpless. If West returns a club, discard your diamond loser, enter your hand with a trump and ruff your fourth heart with dummy's nine of spades. No other return by West can do you any harm either.

If East trumps his partner's good heart at trick four and returns a diamond, win the ace, cash one high spade, and ruff your last heart in dummy. Now you can discard your diamond on the king of clubs.

Admittedly, you have to be a bit lucky, but you might as well play for some luck rather than give up altogether.

NOBLESSE OBLIGE

Neither side vulnerable

Dealer East

North

♠ K J 2
♥ Q J 2
♦ 10 9 7
♣ 10 9 8 7

South

♠ 5 3
♥ A 9 8 7 6 5
♦ A 3 2
♣ A K

East	South	West	North
Pass	1 ♥	Pass	2 ♥
Pass	4 ♥	All Pass	

Opening lead: Eight of diamonds

You cover in dummy and duck East's jack. East continues with the king of diamonds, which you win. At trick three you lead a low spade, West also plays low. Which spade do you play from dummy and why?

Solution

North

♠ K J 2
♥ Q J 2
♦ 10 9 7
♣ 10 9 8 7

West

♠ A 9 8 6
♥ 10 3
♦ 8 6 4
♣ Q J 5 4

East

♠ Q 10 7 4
♥ K 4
♦ K Q J 5
♣ 6 3 2

South

♠ 5 3
♥ A 9 8 7 6 5
♦ A 3 2
♣ A K

In order to realize this ambitious contract you must find the king of hearts in the East hand. Assuming he has that card along with the six high card points he is marked for in diamonds, it should be obvious that East cannot also possess the ace of spades and not open the bidding. Therefore, West has the ace of spades (if the hand is makeable), and the proper play is the *king*.

HANDLE WITH CARE

North

♠ J 2
♥ J 10 9 8 3
♦ 6 5
♣ K Q J 8

South

♠ A K 10 9 8
♥ A K 2
♦ K Q
♣ A 9 7

It would be difficult to arrive at contract of six no trump so let's pretend you did. West leads the deuce of clubs. Plan the play.

Solution

North

♠ J 2
♥ J 10 9 8 3
♦ 6 5
♣ K Q J 8

West	East
♠ 6 3	♠ Q 7 5 4
♥ Q 7 4	♥ 6 5
♦ A 10 3 2	♦ J 9 8 7 4
♣ 10 4 3 2	♣ 6 5

South

♠ A K 10 9 8
♥ A K 2
♦ K Q
♣ A 9 7

You must combine the heart and spade suits to give yourself the best chance. Proper technique is to win the club ace, cash the heart ace, and then lead a *diamond* honor.

Assuming the diamond loses and a diamond is returned (as good as anything), cash a second high heart. If the queen falls, you have twelve tricks; if it does not, enter dummy with a club and run the jack of spades.

This line wins if the queen of hearts is either lonesome or doubleton, or if East has no more than four spades headed by the queen. The key play, incidentally, is the diamond honor early. If you neglect to establish a diamond trick and play off the ace-king of hearts first, you might find that when you go to establish your twelfth trick in diamonds (assuming the spade finesse works) that the player with the ace of diamonds also has a good heart to cash.

You simply must get one diamond trick early unless both major suit queens cooperate. Who ever heard of two women cooperating over anything?

TEMPTATION

East-West vulnerable

Dealer North

North

♠ Q 5
♥ Q 6 5
♦ Q 4
♣ A Q 10 8 6 4

South

♠ A K
♥ A 7 4 2
♦ A 7 6 3 2
♣ J 2

North	East	South	West
1 ♣	Pass	1 ♦	Pass
2 ♣	Pass	3 NT	All Pass

Opening lead: Six of spades

You win and play the jack of clubs, West playing the seven and East the five. You continue with a second club and West plays the three. Now what?

Solution

North
♠ Q 5
♥ Q 6 5
♦ Q 4
♣ A Q 10 8 6 4

West	East
♠ J 9 7 6 2	♠ 10 8 4 3
♥ K 10 8	♥ J 9 3
♦ J 5	♦ K 10 9 8
♣ K 7 3	♣ 9 5

South
♠ A K
♥ A 7 4 2
♦ A 7 6 3 2
♣ J 2

You should play the *ace!* If East has the king of clubs and you finesse a second time, he will win and play a spade. You are now kaput. On the other hand, if you go up with the ace and play a third club, discarding your *ace* of spades, East will have absolutely no return to keep you out of dummy.

But what if the finesse worked all along as it does in the diagram? That, admittedly, could be a bit embarrassing. However, even if West does have the king of clubs, you still make the contract if West owns either red king.

Let's follow the play. You win the ace of clubs and play a third club, discarding your remaining spade honor, as the kibitzers move in a bit closer. West dare not play a spade, so he will probably lead from the suit in which he does not have the king. You put up dummy's queen, and if East covers, duck, and win the second round of the suit. Now lead up to your other red queen. If there is a God in heaven, West will have one of those red kings and your great play will not go unrewarded.

Finally, if you didn't see what this problem was all about and innocently repeated the club finesse you made your contract plus overtricks—and I might add you are probably the type of person who could walk across a freeway in the middle of traffic without getting scratched.

ALMOST RIDICULOUS

North-South vulnerable

Dealer South

North

♠ K 10 2
♥ A 3
♦ 10 8 4 2
♣ K 5 4 3

South

♠ A Q J 5
♥ 10 8 7 4
♦ A K 5
♣ A 2

After you open one spade and partner responds two clubs, East bids two hearts. You double and your partner removes to two spades. Picturing your partner with heart shortage you embark on a sequence that is too embarrassing to put in print. Suffice it to say that the final contract of six spades is mercifully undoubled.

West leads the six of hearts, which you win with dummy's ace, and return a heart to East's jack, West playing the deuce. East now shifts to the six of diamonds which you win, West playing the seven. You lead a heart and West ruffs with the three of spades. You overruff with dummy's ten and from here on in you are on your own. Can you see any way at all out of this mess?

Solution

North

♠ K 10 2
♥ A 3
♦ 10 8 4 2
♣ K 5 4 3

West	East
♠ 8 3	♠ 9 7 6 4
♥ 6 2	♥ K Q J 9 5
♦ J 9 7 3	♦ Q 6
♣ J 9 8 7 6	♣ Q 10

South

♠ A Q J 5
♥ 10 8 7 4
♦ A K 5
♣ A 2

The only possible way to make this slam is to ruff two hearts in dummy and squeeze West in the minors. In order to do this, West must have five clubs and either four diamonds or the queen-jack of diamonds. The first case is more probable, as East should have some honors and some distribution to justify his two level overcall.

Once you commit yourself to play West for four diamonds and five clubs you should play as follows: Cash the king of spades, enter your hand with a club, and ruff your last heart. Now back to your hand with a second round of diamonds, draw the remaining trumps, and on the last trump West will be squeezed. The key play is cashing the *king of spades* to remove West's last trump so he cannot uppercut dummy again when you try to ruff your last heart.

You and your partner really bid beautifully.

NO SUPPORT

North-South vulnerable

Dealer West

North

♠ None
♥ J 10 8 7 6
♦ Q J 8 7 6
♣ 10 5 4

South

♠ J 10 9 8 4 3 2
♥ A K Q
♦ 10
♣ A 3

West	North	East	South
1 NT*	Pass	Pass	2 ♠
Dbl.	All Pass		

*16-18

Opening lead: King of clubs

You allow the lead to hold as East signals violently with the nine. West obediently continues with the queen which you capture. What is your next play?

Solution

North
♠ None
♥ J 10 8 7 6
♦ Q J 8 7 6
♣ 10 5 4

West	East
♠ A K Q 7	♠ 6 5
♥ 9 3 2	♥ 5 4
♦ A 5 4	♦ K 9 3 2
♣ K Q 2	♣ J 9 8 7 6

South
♠ J 10 9 8 4 3 2
♥ A K Q
♦ 10
♣ A 3

Things are not quite as rosy as they look. You have five top losers and are in grave danger of losing a sixth if West can somehow promote his fourth trump.

That "somehow" is accomplished by simply having East lead a fourth round of clubs before trumps have all been removed. By refusing to overruff if you ruff high West insures making four trump tricks.

Assume a top spade is played at trick three. West wins and plays a third club, which you ruff. You play a second middle spade. West wins, and can either underlead his ace of diamonds now or later when in with the third spade to promote his seven of trumps when East leads that killing fourth club.

The way to avoid all this nonsense is to lead a *diamond* at trick three. This will remove East's lone entry prematurely. No overruff is available, and you breeze home, losing but three spades, a club, and a diamond.

SURE THING

North

♠ 6 4
♥ A 10 4 3
♦ A Q 4
♣ K 10 3 2

South

♠ A J
♥ K Q 9 8 7
♦ K 5
♣ A 8 5 4

Contract: 6 ♥

Opening lead: Five of spades

East furnishes the queen. Trumps are 2-2. Can you find the sure trick play?

Solution

North

♠ 6 4
♥ A 10 4 3
♦ A Q 4
♣ K 10 3 2

West

♠ K 10 7 5 3
♥ J 2
♦ J 9 8 7 6
♣ 6

East

♠ Q 9 8 2
♥ 6 5
♦ 10 3 2
♣ Q J 9 7

South

♠ A J
♥ K Q 9 8 7
♦ K 5
♣ A 8 5 4

The sure trick play is to win the spade ace, draw trumps, discard the jack of spades on the third diamond, ruff dummy's last spade, and lead a low club.

If West plays low, insert the ten. If East wins, he must return a club. If clubs are 3-2 there are no further problems, and if East has all the remaining clubs he cannot take a trick regardless of which club he plays.

If, when you lead a club towards dummy, West plays an honor, you can either play low and claim, or win the king and lead a low club to the eight if East follows.

You shouldn't limp home lame on this one.

AMBITIOUS

North

♠ 9 6 3
♥ A 8 7 6 5
♦ 4 3 2
♣ K 9

South

♠ A K Q J 5
♥ 9
♦ A 5
♣ A Q 10 5 4

After a series of bids in which your partner misleads you (again) you arrive at a contract of only seven spades.

West leads the queen of hearts to dummy's ace. You play the ace-king of spades and East follows with the ten on the second round. How do you continue?

Solution

North

♠ 9 6 3
♥ A 8 7 6 5
♦ 4 3 2
♣ K 9

West

♠ 8 7 4
♥ Q
♦ K J 9 8 7
♣ J 6 3 2

East

♠ 10 2
♥ K J 10 4 2
♦ Q 10 6
♣ 8 7

South

♠ A K Q J 5
♥ 9
♦ A 5
♣ A Q 10 5 4

The only way to make this hand is to be able to get rid of two of dummy's diamonds on your clubs. In order to do this clubs must break 4-2 and the player with the long trump must have the four clubs.

As West appears to be the player with the long trump he must be assumed to have the four clubs. Lead a club to the *nine* at trick four, cash the king of clubs, enter your hand with a diamond, play off two high clubs discarding diamonds, and ruff a diamond. Ruff a heart high back to your hand, draw the last trump, and your ten of clubs will stand up as trick number thirteen.

Not only have you played the hand well but you have even catered to West leading a singleton heart, as you never risked ruffing a heart with the five of spades.

TO FINESSE OR NOT TO FINESSE

North
♠ 9 6 4 3
♥ A Q
♦ A K J 10 9
♣ A Q

South
♠ A K Q J 8 2
♥ 4 3
♦ 3 2
♣ 9 7 5

(a) How should you play a contract of 6 ♠ with a low heart lead? (I don't know why I am so good to you.)

(b) How should you play a contract of seven spades with the same lead?

(Spades are 2-1)

Solution

North

♠ 9 6 4 3
♥ A Q
♦ A K J 10 9
♣ A Q

West	East
♠ 10 7	♠ 5
♥ J 9 8 2	♥ K 10 7 6 5
♦ 7 6	♦ Q 8 5 4
♣ K 8 4 3 2	♣ J 10 6

South

♠ A K Q J 8 2
♥ 4 3
♦ 3 2
♣ 9 7 5

(a) In six spades, win with the heart ace, draw trump and makes a loser-on-loser play in diamonds by playing the ace-king and jack, discarding a heart if not covered. Assuming the diamond play loses, you still have two more club discards coming on the top diamonds.

(b) In seven, rise with the ace of hearts, draw trumps and play to establish the diamond suit for a heart discard by ruffing, and eventually take the club finesse unless, of course, the queen of diamonds drops singleton or doubleton. (Never happens for you, just for the other guy, right?)

THE CRYSTAL BALL

East-West vulnerable

Dealer North

North

♠ 7 5
♥ K Q 2
♦ A Q 10 2
♣ K J 10 4

South

♠ Q J 6 3
♥ A 5 4 3
♦ 6
♣ A 9 8 3

North	South
1 ♦	1 ♥
2 ♥	2 NT
3 NT	Pass

Opening lead: Deuce of spades

East plays the ten and you the queen. Now what?

Solution

North
♠ 7 5
♥ K Q 2
♦ A Q 10 2
♣ K J 10 4

West
♠ A K 9 2
♥ J 9 8
♦ J 8 7
♣ Q 6 5

East
♠ 10 8 4
♥ 10 7 6
♦ K 9 5 4 3
♣ 7 2

South
♠ Q J 6 3
♥ A 5 4 3
♦ 6
♣ A 9 8 3

Obviously, you must take the club finesse into West, since you don't want East leading through your spade holding. For one thing, West might have started with five spades (unlikely because he didn't bid and led the deuce), or he might make the mistake of cashing the ace-king of spades if he does have the queen of clubs. (Also very unlikely, as he will be able to tell from his partner's second spade whether or not his spades cash.)

But you must look even further ahead. What if the club finesse loses, West cashes one spade, and then shifts to a diamond? Are you going to finesse? You might need the finesse if the hearts don't break. On the other hand, if they do break you don't need the diamond finesse.

Therefore, the solution is to *test the hearts* before taking the club finesse. If they break 3-3 you can refuse the diamond finesse (you have nine tricks without it), and if they don't, you must take the diamond finesse.

IMPENDING DOOM

East-West vulnerable

Dealer North

North

♠ J 9 8 7
♥ K 10 9 6
♦ 2
♣ A K 7 5

South

♠ A K 6 5
♥ Q J 8 7 5
♦ 10 8
♣ 4 3

North	East	South	West
1 ♣	3 ♦	3 ♥	Pass
4 ♥	All Pass		

Opening lead: Five of diamonds

East wins the king and shifts to the deuce of spades. Plan the play.

Solution

North
♠ J 9 8 7
♥ K 10 9 6
♦ 2
♣ A K 7 5

West
♠ Q 10 4 3
♥ A 4
♦ Q 6 5
♣ Q 10 9 6

East
♠ 2
♥ 3 2
♦ A K J 9 7 4 3
♣ J 8 2

South
♠ A K 6 5
♥ Q J 8 7 5
♦ 10 8
♣ 4 3

The danger, that even the kibitzers can sense, is that East has shifted to a singleton spade. What with West marked with the trump ace, it is possible to foresee that West will win the first trump lead, give East a spade ruff, and after East exits with a minor suit card you are going to be stuck with another spade loser.

This can be avoided. Win the spade return, ruff a diamond, and play ace-king and ruff a club. Now play a tricky jack of hearts. West is too old for that one, so he wins the ace and gives East his spade ruff. But East remains with only diamonds. His return gives you a ruff-sluff, so you make your contract.

Incidentally, it is pointless to ruff both of dummy's clubs before leading a trump. If East has 1-2-6-4 distribution, West will overruff the fourth club, give East a spade ruff, and East will have a trump with which to exit.

Furthermore, if East is 1-1-7-4, the recommended line works fine, as East will not have a trump if West leads a second round of spades.

RATING SCALE

250 - 200	SOMETHING ELSE
195 - 150	NEAR-EXPERT
145 - 100	DON'T FEEL BAD
95 - 50	DON'T FEEL GOOD
LESS	SOMETHING ELSE

FAVORABLE LEAD

North

♠ A 7 5
♥ A Q 9 5
♦ K J 8 4
♣ 6 3

South

♠ 9 4 2
♥ K 10 7 6
♦ A
♣ A K Q 9 4

Contract: 6 ♥

Even though the only unbid suit is spades, West leads the seven of diamonds. You win and play a trump to the queen, East playing the eight. How do you continue?

Solution

North

♠ A 7 5
♥ A Q 9 5
♦ K J 8 4
♣ 6 3

West

♠ Q 10
♥ J 4 3 2
♦ 7 6 3
♣ J 10 5 2

East

♠ K J 8 6 3
♥ 8
♦ Q 10 9 5 2
♣ 8 7

South

♠ 9 4 2
♥ K 10 7 6
♦ A
♣ A K Q 9 4

Simply ruff a low diamond with the *ten* of hearts, play the king, finesse the nine of hearts if necessary, and draw the last trump, discarding a spade from your hand.

Now duck a club, and you make the contract if clubs break no worse than 4-2, or if the queen of diamonds drops third.

If it turns out that East was kidding with that eight of hearts and actually started with Jxxx, you must still play four rounds of hearts, conceding a trick to East's jack. You now need clubs to be 3-3 or miracle of miracles, the J 10 doubleton. Don't hold your breath.

Also, don't take credit unless you ruffed a low diamond with the ten of hearts.

FINESSES IN ALL SUITS

Neither side vulnerable

Dealer South

North

♠ A Q 7 6 4 3
♥ J 3 2
♦ 4
♣ K J 2

South

♠ 10
♥ Q 10 9 8 7 6
♦ A Q 10
♣ A 9 3

South	West	North	East
1 ♥	2 ♦	2 ♠	Pass
3 ♥	Pass	4 ♠	All Pass

Opening lead: King of hearts

West continues with the ace of trumps, all following, and then switches to the nine of spades. Plan the play.

Solution

North
♠ A Q 7 6 4 3
♥ J 3 2
♦ 4
♣ K J 2

West	East
♠ 9 2	♠ K J 8 5
♥ A K	♥ 5 4
♦ K J 9 8 7 6	♦ 5 3 2
♣ 10 5 4	♣ Q 8 7 6

South
♠ 10
♥ Q 10 9 8 7 6
♦ A Q 10
♣ A 9 3

Win the ace of spades and ruff a spade. Now the big play—the queen of diamonds!

Assuming West wins, he will be end-played, and forced to lead a club. (A diamond or a spade gives you the hand automatically.) You play low from dummy. If East plays the queen you have the rest. If East plays the ten, win the ace, play the ace of diamonds, discarding a spade, and ruff a diamond. Now ruff a spade. If the king has not dropped you have no alternative but to finesse the jack of clubs.

CONTROL YOURSELF

Neither side vulnerable

Dealer East

North

♠ 7 2
♥ A 8 7 4 3
♦ 6 5
♣ K 8 7 5

South

♠ K Q 10 9 8 4
♥ K Q J
♦ 4
♣ A 3 2

East	South	West	North
1 ♦	Dbl.	4 ♦	Dbl.
Pass	4 ♠	Dbl.	All Pass

Opening lead: Three of diamonds

East wins the ten of diamonds and continues with the ace, West playing the deuce. Plan the play.

Solution

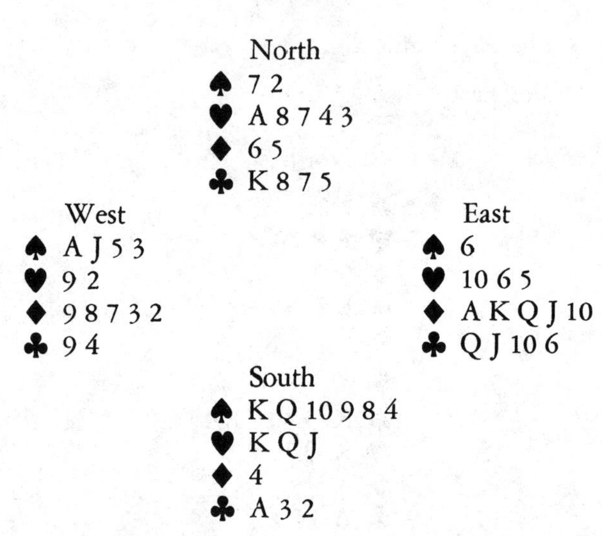

You must assume that West has AJxx of spades for his double, or else what is he doing? If that is the case there is a grave danger that you could lose control of the hand.

Assume you ruff the diamond at trick two and lead a high spade. West ducks. If you continue spades, West can establish a trick with his lowly five of spades by simply forcing you to ruff diamonds each time he wins a spade trick.

Therefore you must plan to lose a spade trick while there is still a trump in dummy to handle a possible diamond force. *Lead a low spade at trick three!*

If West wins the jack, he can no longer force you in diamonds, as you can ruff in dummy and simply knock out his remaining high spade after entering your hand with a heart. If West ducks the spade, lead a high spade to West's ace. Ruff the diamond return, cash the other high spade, and run the hearts, discarding the losing club. West can make no more than his jack of spades.

This is, in fact, a remarkable deal. Against diamond forces South must duck a spade. However, if West leads either a heart or a club, South must immediately lead a *diamond* to break up the communications between East and West — in the first case, to prevent East from giving West a heart ruff, and in the second to prevent East from cashing an established club trick.

HOW DID WE GET THERE?

North

♠ Q 10 8 7 5 3 2
♥ A
♦ J 9 7 3 2
♣ None

South

♠ A
♥ K Q J 5 3 2
♦ A K 4
♣ A K 4

After West deals and opens with a non-vulnerable preempt of three clubs you settle comfortably in a contract of *seven* hearts!

West leads the queen of clubs. Plan the play.

Solutior

North

♠ Q 10 8 7 5 3 2
♥ A
♦ J 9 7 3 2
♣ None

West	East
♠ None	♠ K J 9 6 4
♥ 10 4	♥ 9 8 7 6
♦ 10 8 6	♦ Q 5
♣ Q J 10 9 7 5 3 2	♣ 8 6

South

♠ A
♥ K Q J 5 3 2
♦ A K 4
♣ A K 4

Win the club lead in your hand, discarding a spade, and plunk down the ace of diamonds. If the queen falls (presumably from West), cash the ace of spades, enter dummy with a heart, and ruff a spade, hoping that the king of spades is doubleton. If it is, draw trumps and use your jack of diamonds as the entry to the queen of spades for the club discard.

If the queen of diamonds does not fall at trick two, enter dummy with a trump and lead a *diamond* back to your hand. In order to make the hand, you need to drop the doubleton queen of diamonds, so there is no need to risk a spade ruff by returning to your hand via the spade ace.

PLAY COOL

North

♠ Q
♥ K 10 9 7 2
♦ 3
♣ K J 9 7 5 4

South

♠ A 10 8 4
♥ A 5
♦ A 7 6
♣ A Q 8 2

Contract: 7 ♣

Opening lead: Queen of diamonds
What is your plan?

Solution

North
♠ Q
♥ K 10 9 7 2
♦ 3
♣ K J 9 7 5 4

West	East
♠ K J 5 3	♠ 9 7 6 2
♥ 8 4	♥ Q J 6 3
♦ Q J 10 4	♦ K 9 8 5 2
♣ 10 6 3	♣ None

South
♠ A 10 8 4
♥ A 5
♦ A 7 6
♣ A Q 8 2

You must be careful to lead a *low* trump at trick two to an honor in dummy. If you carelessly lead a high trump from your hand and find West with all the trumps plus a doubleton heart (the only distribution you fear), you will be unable to establish the heart suit, as West will make the ten of clubs on an overruff.

However, if you lead a low trump at trick two and West does have all the trumps, you can still establish hearts by ruffing high in your own hand twice, eventually finessing the nine of clubs to draw West's last two trumps.

Incidentally, if both opponents follow to the first round of trumps you should play the ace of hearts and, unless an honor drops, play a second heart to the king before drawing the last trump. Hearts might be 5-1 and the player with the five hearts might just hold the odd trump.

LOOKS EASY

Both sides vulnerable

Dealer South

North

♠ A 10
♥ A Q J 9 8 4
♦ 2
♣ 9 8 6 3

South

♠ Q J 5
♥ None
♦ A K Q 4 3
♣ A Q 7 5 4

South	North
1 ♦	1 ♥
2 ♣	3 ♥
3 NT	Pass

Opening lead: Deuce of spades

You try the ten from dummy, East produces the king and returns the three to dummy's ace. The nine of clubs is covered by the ten, queen, and king. Back comes a spade. Plan the play.

Solution

North
♠ A 10
♥ A Q J 9 8 4
♦ 2
♣ 9 8 6 3

West	East
♠ 9 6 4 2	♠ K 8 7 3
♥ K 10 7 3	♥ 6 5 2
♦ 10 9	♦ J 8 7 6 5
♣ K J 2	♣ 10

South
♠ Q J 5
♥ None
♦ A K Q 4 3
♣ A Q 7 5 4

Only a greedy man would go down on this hand, as there are nine tricks for the taking, assuming that spades are 4-4 (which they should be from the lead and return).

The answer is to lead a *low club* at this point and let them cash a second club and long spade. You now have an entry to dummy to cash your ace of hearts and a hand reentry in the form of dummy's fourth club.

Look what happens if you cash your ace of clubs and someone shows out. You give up a club, and the opponents cash their spade and get out with a diamond. Now you can get to dummy with a club to score your ace of hearts, but you cannot get back to your hand to make your long club. If you give up on dummy's ace of hearts you must lose a diamond at the end.

SKILL TESTER

Neither side vulnerable

Dealer South

North
♠ J 3
♥ K 6 5
♦ K 10 3 2
♣ A 7 6 4

South
♠ 9 4
♥ A 10 9 4 3
♦ A Q J
♣ Q 10 2

South	West	North	East
1 ♥	1 ♠	2 ♣	2 ♠
3 ♣	Pass	3 ♥	Pass
4 ♥	All Pass		

Opening lead: King of spades

West continues with the queen of spades, East echoing high-low. At trick three West shifts to the eight of diamonds. Assuming hearts break 3-2 and the queen-jack of hearts is not doubleton, can you see any way of making this hand?

Solution

North
♠ J 3
♥ K 6 5
♦ K 10 3 2
♣ A 7 6 4

West	East
♠ K Q 10 5 2	♠ A 8 7 6
♥ J 2	♥ Q 8 7
♦ 8 4	♦ 9 7 6 5
♣ K 9 5 3	♣ J 8

South
♠ 9 4
♥ A 10 9 4 3
♦ A Q J
♣ Q 10 2

Once you discover that there is a trump loser, the only legitimate way of making this hand is to force the opponents to lead clubs first. This isn't so easy to do. However, a little imagination always helps.

If West, who is pretty well marked with the king of clubs (East should have the ace of spades), has a doubleton honor in hearts there is hope — providing his diamonds can be removed.

The proper play is to cash a *second diamond.* Then; a heart to the king and a heart to the ten. If If West has a doubleton in each red suit as well as the king of clubs, he has no safe return.

What, you might ask, will happen if West has a third diamond? The answer is that the hand could never have been made. You see, if you play three diamonds before feeding West his heart trick he can get out with a spade, forcing you to ruff in dummy and also forcing you to play clubs from dummy. But, if he plays a spade in the diagrammed hand you can ruff in dummy, enter your hand with a diamond, draw the last trump and reenter dummy with the ace of clubs to shed your last club on dummy's fourth diamond.

A TOUCHY GRAND

North

♠ K 2
♥ A Q 10
♦ A K 3
♣ A 7 6 5 4

South

♠ A J 9 6 5 4 3
♥ K J
♦ 8 7 6 5
♣ None

Contract: 7 ♠

Opening lead: Nine of hearts

What are your first two plays?

Solution

North
♠ K 2
♥ A Q 10
♦ A K 3
♣ A 7 6 5 4

West	East
♠ None	♠ Q 10 8 7
♥ 9 8 7 6	♥ 5 4 3 2
♦ Q 10 4 2	♦ J 9
♣ Q 10 8 3 2	♣ K J 9

South
♠ A J 9 6 5 4 3
♥ K J
♦ 8 7 6 5
♣ None

For openers you must take out a little insurance against all four trumps on your right. Win the *queen* of *hearts* and *ruff a club*. Now a spade to the king. If everyone follows, lead a spade to the ace repeating after yourself "eight ever, nine never".

However, if, when you lead a spade to the king West shows out, your club ruff at trick two is going to come in handy. Lead a spade to the nine, a diamond to the king, and play the ace of clubs, discarding a diamond. Ruff a club, back to dummy with a diamond, ruff another club, and finally overtake the king of hearts and cash the ten of hearts, discarding your last diamond. Your last two cards are the A J of trumps and East's are the Q 10. With the lead in dummy, East is rendered helpless.

BRAVE RAISE

North-South vulnerable

Dealer West

North

♠ Q J 4 3 2
♥ J 4 3
♦ 6 5 3
♣ 7 5

South

♠ A 7 6
♥ A K Q 10 9
♦ A 4
♣ K 10 3

West	North	East	South
1 ♦	Pass	Pass	Dbl.
Pass	1 ♠	Pass	3 ♥
Pass	4 ♥	All Pass	

Opening lead: King of diamonds

Your partner must think you play almost as well as you think you do. East plays the eight of diamonds at trick one. What is your plan to justify this touching faith in your declarer play?

Solution

North
♠ Q J 4 3 2
♥ J 4 3
♦ 6 5 3
♣ 7 5

West
♠ K 9 8
♥ 7 6 5
♦ K Q J 7 2
♣ A J

East
♠ 10 5
♥ 8 2
♦ 10 9 8
♣ Q 9 8 6 4 2

South
♠ A 7 6
♥ A K Q 10 9
♦ A 4
♣ K 10 3

First, you must *duck* the opening lead to get any credit at all for this hand. You simply cannot risk establishing a diamond entry for East to lead through your king of clubs once West gets in with the king of spades.

Second, you must play *two* high trumps from your hand after winning the probable diamond continuation, and then lead a *low* spade.

Assuming West has the doubleton king of spades, he must take the trick, and cannot score more than his ace of clubs. If he has three spades to the king and ducks the trick, you must play to the ace of spades and then a third spade. As long as West also has the third trump everything is still hunky-dory. However, if East has the third trump he could ruff his partner's trick and lead a club through, but that wouldn't be very polite. In any case there is nothing you can do about it, so why worry?

LOOK CLOSELY

Neither side vulnerable
Dealer North

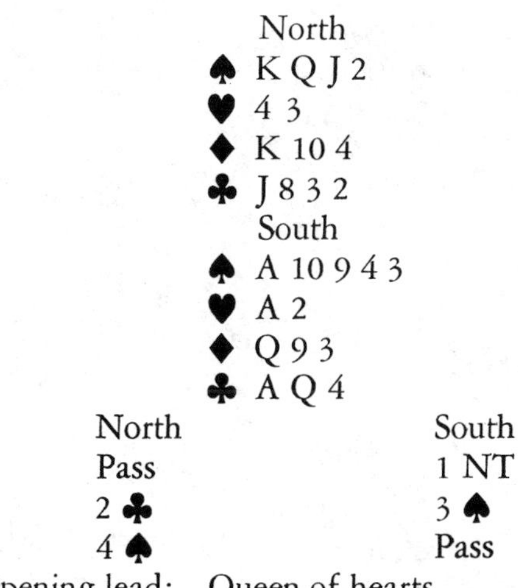

Opening lead: Queen of hearts

This is a bad hand to insert the bidding. Some readers will wonder why South didn't open one spade? If South opens one spade, others will smirk and wonder why he didn't open one no trump. Damned if you do and damned if you don't.

You win the first trick, East playing the nine. You remove trumps in three rounds, East discarding a heart and a diamond after following to the first trump. Now what?

Solution

North

♠ K Q J 2
♥ 4 3
♦ K 10 4
♣ J 8 3 2

West	East
♠ 8 7 6	♠ 5
♥ Q J 10 7 6	♥ K 9 8 5
♦ A 8 7	♦ J 6 5 2
♣ 7 6	♣ K 10 9 5

South

♠ A 10 9 4 3
♥ A 2
♦ Q 9 3
♣ A Q 4

Finesse the queen of clubs, and if this holds, cash the ace. Now exit with a heart. *Do not* play a third club. (If clubs are 4-2, East can cash a heart and exit with a fourth club, forcing you to go a-hunting for the diamond jack.)

Whoever wins the heart must either (1) give you a ruff-sluff, (2) attack diamonds, or (3) set up a club for a diamond discard if a third club is played.

If the club finesse loses, you must hope that either clubs break or that you can guess the location of the jack of diamonds if they don't.

VISUALIZE

Both sides vulnerable

Dealer West

North

♠ A Q 10 2
♥ 10 6 4 3
♦ 9 7 5 3
♣ K

South

♠ K J 3
♥ A J 9
♦ K J 2
♣ A 9 4 3

West	North	East	South
1 ♣	Pass	Pass	Dbl.
Pass	1 ♠	Pass	1 NT
2 ♣	2 ♥	Pass	2 ♠
Pass	2 NT	Pass	3 NT
All Pass			

Opening lead: Queen of clubs

You win smartly in dummy, East playing the deuce, and lead a heart to the jack and king. West continues with the ten of clubs, East plays the five and you duck, discarding a diamond from dummy. West exits with the nine of spades. Plan the play.

Solution

North

♠ A Q 10 2
♥ 10 6 4 3
♦ 9 7 5 3
♣ K

West	East
♠ 9 7	♠ 8 6 5 4
♥ K Q 5	♥ 8 7 2
♦ A Q	♦ 10 8 6 4
♣ Q J 10 8 7 6	♣ 5 2

South

♠ K J 3
♥ A J 9
♦ K J 2
♣ A 9 4 3

You should assume West has all the missing goodies for his vulnerable bidding. With this in mind, win the queen of spades, play a spade to the king, hopefully removing all of West's spades, and then the ace and nine of hearts.

If the cards behave properly, West, upon winning the queen of hearts, will be forced to give you your ninth trick by switching to either minor, unless he produces a third spade or a fourth heart.

Even so you have the last laugh. Cash your major suit winners and lead a diamond to the jack. West must have the bare ace! Count. If West has a third spade to go along with his three hearts and six clubs that leaves him at most one diamond. The same holds true if he plays a fourth heart. Again he can have no more than one diamond. God, you're a great player!

CONSERVATIVE BIDDING

North

♠ K Q J 10 9
♥ A Q 3 2
♦ 2
♣ K Q 4

South

♠ A 8 7
♥ 6 5 4
♦ A K Q 9 8 7 6
♣ None

West opens the bidding with four clubs, partner doubles, East passes and you eventually sign off at seven diamonds! West leads the ace of clubs (he doesn't trust you) and you ruff concealing a smirk.

You play the ace of diamonds and West plays the jack. On the king of diamonds West discards a club, not concealing a smirk. How do you play to make West pay for that last smirk?

Solution

North
♠ K Q J 10 9
♥ A Q 3 2
♦ 2
♣ K Q 4

West
♠ 6 5 3
♥ 10
♦ J
♣ A J 10 9 8 7 6 5

East
♠ 4 2
♥ K J 9 8 7
♦ 10 5 4 3
♣ 3 2

South
♠ A 8 7
♥ 6 5 4
♦ A K Q 9 8 7 6
♣ None

You would like to make this grand slam by couping East without risking the heart finesse. You can do this if you time your plays carefully and East is polite enough to hold at least two spades and two clubs (or three spades and one club).

At trick four enter dummy with a spade and ruff a good club; back to dummy with a spade, and lead a second high club. East must discard, and you jettison your ace of spades, enticing the kibitzers a bit closer to the table.

Now start playing good spades through East. If East trumps, you overtrump and have enough heart discards after drawing the last trump. Therefore, East must discard hearts. You discard two hearts and ruff the fifth spade.

Enter dummy with the ace of hearts and you will have the Q 9 of diamonds over East's 10 5 with just two cards remaining. The kibitzers will surely give you a sitting ovation and West will never smirk at you again.

TWO TEN CARD FITS

North-South vulnerable

Dealer West

North

♠ 3 2
♥ K J 7 6
♦ A 10
♣ J 10 6 5 4

South

♠ A
♥ Q 2
♦ Q J 7 6 5
♣ A Q 9 7 3

West	North	East	South
Pass	Pass	Pass	1 ♦
2 ♦*	Dbl.	3 ♠	4 ♣
Pass	5 ♣	All Pass	

*Weak major two-suiter

Opening lead: King of spades

Play your play.

Solution

North
♠ 3 2
♥ K J 7 6
♦ A 10
♣ J 10 6 5 4

West		East
♠ K Q J 7 5		♠ 10 9 8 6 4
♥ 10 9 5 4 3		♥ A 8
♦ 4 3		♦ K 9 8 2
♣ K		♣ 8 2

South
♠ A
♥ Q 2
♦ Q J 7 6 5
♣ A Q 9 7 3

The idea is to avoid the club finesse, if possible, by first stripping the major suits, cashing the club ace, and then end-playing East, even if he happens to hold the guarded king of clubs.

In order to do all of this, your first play should be the queen of hearts, overtaking if West plays low. It should be mentioned that it is very unlikely West has the ace of hearts, judging from his original pass and lack of further competition. If he does, the club finesse is sure to succeed.

If East wins the ace of hearts and returns a spade(what you want), ruff, cash the ace of clubs, and if no king appears, lead a heart to dummy, ruff a heart, and exit with a club. East should be endplayed.

The reason you overtook the queen of hearts at trick two was to prevent a clever East player from ducking the first heart, winning the second, and leading a trump before you have been able to ruff a spade. If East ducks the first heart, ruff a spade, and exit with a heart. If East wins and returns a trump, play the ace using the same plan mentioned above.

Granted, it is unlikely East is going to do all of this but you must at least try to strip the majors before tackling trumps. Giving yourself a double shot by laying down the ace of clubs increases your chances immeasurably — if you were able to ruff a spade first!

TWENTY-EIGHT POINT SLAM

Both sides vulnerable

Dealer South

North

♠ Q J 9 8
♥ A J 9 8 5 4
♦ None
♣ Q J 3

South

♠ A K 10 2
♥ None
♦ A K 8 6 4 3
♣ K 6 2

South	North
1 ♦	1 ♥
1 ♠	4 ♠
6 ♠	Pass

Opening lead: Ten of clubs

East wins the ace and returns the five of clubs, West playing the nine. Plan the play.

Solution

North
♠ Q J 9 8
♥ A J 9 8 5 4
♦ None
♣ Q J 3

West		East
♠ 7 6 4 3		♠ 5
♥ K 10		♥ Q 7 6 3 2
♦ Q 10		♦ J 9 7 5 2
♣ 10 9 8 7 4		♣ A 5

South
♠ A K 10 2
♥ None
♦ A K 8 6 4 3
♣ K 6 2

This is a problem in addition. If you can make it up to twelve, you should see that all you have to do is ruff one heart with your deuce of spades, and you are home, provided diamonds go twice.

Win the club return in dummy and play the ace of hearts, discarding a diamond, then ruff a heart with that deuce of spades; cash two top diamonds, and crossruff. Even if West ruffs the second diamond you still make the hand if clubs were 4-3 originally.

Notice that if you fall into the trap of cashing your top diamonds and ruffing a diamond prematurely, West sheds a heart on the third diamond, and now you can no longer ruff a heart with your deuce of spades.

It is true with the given lie of the cards you could draw one trump, collect a second club trick, and then crossruff, but that is strictly double dummy and definitely not the proper line of play.

GREED

Neither side vulnerable

Dealer North

North

♠ A 3
♥ 10 2
♦ J 6 3
♣ A K 9 7 5 4

South

♠ Q 9 7 2
♥ Q 9 7
♦ A K 2
♣ Q 10 3

North	South
1 ♣	2 NT
3 NT	Pass

Opening lead: Five of spades

Do you win the ace at trick one?

If so, what do you play at trick two?

If not, what is your plan?

Solution

North
♠ A 3
♥ 10 2
♦ J 6 3
♣ A K 9 7 5 4

West	East
♠ J 8 6 5 4	♠ K 10
♥ A 8 4 3	♥ K J 6 5
♦ 10 7 5 4	♦ Q 9 8
♣ None	♣ J 8 6 2

South
♠ Q 9 7 2
♥ Q 9 7
♦ A K 2
♣ Q 10 3

Of course you should win the ace of spades at trick one. If clubs divide in any fashion but 4-0 with the length in the East hand, you have nine sure ones.

The key to the hand is the proper play at trick two. Lead a *low club to the queen.* You cannot guard against four clubs to the jack in the East hand by leading a top club from dummy, because you do not have a dummy reentry. Assume you lead a high club from dummy at trick two and West shows out. What can you do? Right, nothing. So forget about guarding against something you cannot handle.

If West shows out on the queen of clubs (the only possible problem), duck a club into the East hand and hope East has both the king of spades and the jack of hearts, in which case the defenders cannot take more than three major suit tricks along with their club trick.

In tournament bridge it would be right to duck the opening lead around to the queen because in the long run it pays to be greedy and try for overtricks in duplicate bridge.

AWKWARD

Neither side vulnerable

Dealer North

North

♠ Q J 10 2
♥ K
♦ Q 7 6
♣ A Q 7 4 2

South

♠ 3
♥ A Q 10 9 7 6 5
♦ J 5 4
♣ K J

North	South
1 ♣	1 ♥
1 ♠	4 ♥
Pass	

Opening lead: Five of clubs

West plays the eight and you win the king. How do you continue?

Solution

North

♠ Q J 10 2
♥ K
♦ Q 7 6
♣ A Q 7 4 2

West	East
♠ A 9 8 7	♠ K 6 5 4
♥ J 4	♥ 8 3 2
♦ K 9 8	♦ A 10 3 2
♣ 10 9 6 5	♣ 8 3

South

♠ 3
♥ A Q 10 9 7 6 5
♦ J 5 4
♣ K J

Your best chance, though it may hurt a bit, is to plunk down the ace and queen of hearts. If the jack does not oblige, fall back on a 3-3 club division by overtaking the jack.

Even if the jack of hearts does not drop and the third club gets ruffed, you still make the hand if you can work out some miracle in diamonds. (For example, East may have a doubleton picture and you can lead the jack originally.)

Even though this line of play seems a bit scary, any other line is even more dangerous and stands even less chance to succeed.

TWO PARTS

North

♠ 9 8 7
♥ A K 7 6 4
♦ 6 5
♣ 7 6 5

South

♠ A K Q J 3 2
♥ 3
♦ A J 7 4 2
♣ A

a. Contract: 5 ♠ Opening lead: King of clubs

b. Contract: 6 ♠ Same lead.

Plan the play in each case.

Solution

North

♠ 9 8 7
♥ A K 7 6 4
♦ 6 5
♣ 7 6 5

West	East
♠ 6 5 4	♠ 10
♥ J 9	♥ Q 10 8 5 2
♦ K Q 10 3	♦ 9 8
♣ K Q J 2	♣ 10 9 8 4 3

South

♠ A K Q J 3 2
♥ 3
♦ A J 7 4 2
♣ A

a. In five spades lead a heart to the ace, a diamond to the ace, and concede a diamond. You can afford to have one of your diamonds overtrumped in dummy and still make your contract. (You could also play the ace and a diamond at trick two. Leading from dummy is a remote safety play against East being void.)

However, take no credit if you played as much as one high trump first. If East, for example, has 10xx of spades and a doubleton diamond, he can overtrump dummy and return his last trump, leaving you stranded with a diamond loser.

b. In a contract of six spades, duck a diamond at trick two. Win any return, and cash exactly one trump before establishing your diamond suit. Drawing one trump is a safety play against either opponent having a doubleton diamond with a singleton spade. (Take a peek at the diagram.)

Playing for the ten of spades to be singleton so that you could establish the hearts by using the spades as entries, is an inferior line and not worthy of a player of your caliber.

TWO SUITER

Both sides vulnerable

Dealer South

North

♠ J 7 3 2
♥ 6 2
♦ A K 8 7 6
♣ J 3

South

♠ A K 6 5 4
♥ 8 5
♦ 2
♣ A 10 6 5 4

South	West	North	East
1 ♣	Pass	1 ♦	1 ♥
1 ♠	3 ♥	3 ♠	Pass
4 ♠	All Pass		

Opening lead: Three of hearts

East wins the ace and returns the seven of hearts to West's nine. West shifts to the three of diamonds. Plan the play.

Solution

North
♠ J 7 3 2
♥ 6 2
♦ A K 8 7 6
♣ J 3

West
♠ Q
♥ K J 9 3
♦ J 9 4 3
♣ K 9 7 2

East
♠ 10 9 8
♥ A Q 10 7 4
♦ Q 10 5
♣ Q 8

South
♠ A K 6 5 4
♥ 8 5
♦ 2
♣ A 10 6 5 4

Win the diamond and ruff a diamond immediately! This play is made just in case the queen of spades drops singleton, in which case you will have enough dummy entries to establish the diamonds, assuming a normal 4-3 division.

Obviously, the hand cannot be made if trumps are 3-1 (unless the queen is singleton), and the hand is cold if trumps are 2-2. If you fail to ruff a diamond at trick four and find the queen of spades singleton, you are going to have to rely upon a good break in clubs, which is less likely than a good break in diamonds.

After you ruff the diamond, play the ace of spades. If the queen falls, draw trump ending in dummy, and play the king of diamonds. If everyone follows, ruff a diamond and claim your contract, conceding a club.

If somehow diamonds turn out to be 5-2, you still make the hand if East has the king-queen of clubs by leading a low club to the ten rather than ruffing a second diamond. If East splits, win and concede a club. If he does not, he gets a club at the end, providing he had four clubs.

RED KINGS IN THE SUNSET

North

♠ A K 8 7 6
♥ J 3
♦ J 9 6 5
♣ A 3

South

♠ Q J 10 5 4
♥ A Q 4 2
♦ A Q 3
♣ 5

Contract: 6 ♠

Opening lead: Queen of clubs

Trumps are 2-1, plan the play.

Solution

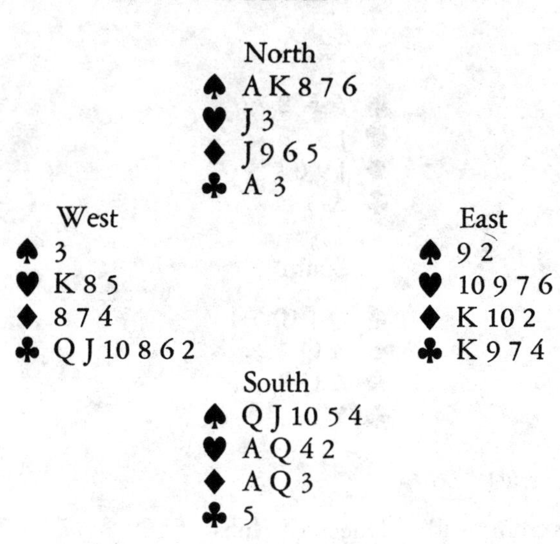

Win the lead, ruff a club, draw trump, and lead a diamond to the queen.

If it loses, you need the heart finesse, no more, no less. But, if the queen of diamonds holds, you are cold if you tackle hearts properly. Obviously, if East has the king of hearts, all you have to do is finesse the queen, but if West has the king, all you have to do is lead up to the jack. If West ducks, he loses his king, and if he goes up, you have two diamond pitches coming on your hearts.

Which is the better play? Leading up to the jack is better because even if East does have the king you can still make the hand on a squeeze if East started with four or more hearts.

Perhaps you noticed something. What if West has ducked the king of diamonds and you lead a heart to the jack and find East with the king of hearts! Well, you must pay off to West's great play and you also know you are in a tough game. Perhaps too tough!

NEVER A LAYDOWN SLAM

North

♠ A 10 4 3
♥ 7 2
♦ A K Q
♣ A J 9 8

South

♠ K
♥ A Q J 10 3
♦ 6 4
♣ K 10 7 6 5

Contract: 6 ♣

Opening lead: Five of diamonds

East plays the deuce. Plan the play.

Solution

North
♠ A 10 4 3
♥ 7 2
♦ A K Q
♣ A J 9 8

West
♠ J 8 5
♥ K 8 5 4
♦ J 9 7 5 3
♣ 3

East
♠ Q 9 7 6 2
♥ 9 6
♦ 10 8 2
♣ Q 4 2

South
♠ K
♥ A Q J 10 3
♦ 6 4
♣ K 10 7 6 5

The best line involves a certain amount of risk — but it is still the best line.

At trick two lead a spade to the king, and then a club to the ace. Assuming everyone follows, cash the ace of spades and ruff a spade. Now cash two diamonds and *run the jack of clubs* even if East shows out. In that case you are reduced to a heart finesse, using a club as an entry.

If the jack of clubs holds, draw the last trump and give up a heart. If West has the doubleton queen of clubs and only three spades, he is endplayed. If West produces a fourth spade, ruff high, and enter dummy with a trump for a heart finesse.

A PUZZLEMENT

North

♠ J 8 7 6
♥ 6 2
♦ Q 5 4
♣ A J 10 9

South

♠ A K
♥ A J 5
♦ A J 10 9 3
♣ Q 5 4

Contract: 3 NT

Opening lead: Four of hearts

East plays the king. Do you take the trick? What is your plan?

Solution

North

♠ J 8 7 6
♥ 6 2
♦ Q 5 4
♣ A J 10 9

West	East
♠ 10 9 3 2	♠ Q 5 4
♥ Q 10 8 4 3	♥ K 9 7
♦ 8	♦ K 7 6 2
♣ K 3 2	♣ 8 7 6

South

♠ A K
♥ A J 5
♦ A J 10 9 3
♣ Q 5 4

This is a tricky devil. Do not risk taking both minor suit finesses. If the diamond finesse works, you have nine tricks without the club finesse. If the club finesse works, you still need the diamond finesse.

Your best play is to *win* the first trick, lead the *queen* of clubs to the ace, and follow with the queen of diamonds. If the finesse loses, you still make the hand if West has the king of clubs or makes the mistake of continuing hearts.

If the queen of diamonds holds, repeat the finesse. If East turns up with four diamonds, then a second club must be led in order to force a dummy entry for the proven diamond finesse.

Now you see why it was important to lead the queen of clubs originally. It was not so much to induce West to cover (anyone who covers the queen looking at that dummy is playing the wrong game) as it was to force a second club entry to dummy in case East started life with four diamonds to the king.

If a low club is led to the ace at trick two, West can defeat the contract by proper management of his clubs later in the play.

TOO GOOD TO BE TRUE

North

♠ A K
♥ J 8 6 5
♦ K 8 7 6
♣ 7 5 3

South

♠ Q 9 8 7 6 5 4
♥ A K 2
♦ None
♣ A Q 6

Contract: 4 ♠

Opening lead: Jack of diamonds

You play low from dummy, East signals, and you ruff. Now what?

Solution

North

♠ A K
♥ J 8 6 5
♦ K 8 7 6
♣ 7 5 3

West	East
♠ None	♠ J 10 3 2
♥ Q 10 9 4 3	♥ 7
♦ J 10 9 3 2	♦ A Q 5 4
♣ K 9 4	♣ J 10 8 2

South

♠ Q 9 8 7 6 5 4
♥ A K 2
♦ None
♣ A Q 6

Your only problem, of course, is if spades are 4-0 and the king of clubs is offside. In order to take out a little insurance against this ghastly possibility you should *cash one high heart at trick two* and lead a spade to dummy.

If both opponents follow, draw trumps as quickly as possible. You have ten top tricks.

However, if someone shows out on the first round of trumps, lead a heart to the king and another heart to the jack. Unless East has specifically four hearts to the queen you will have established a heart for a club discard, and the most you can lose is a heart, a club, and a trump.

Notice how important it is to lead the *second* round of hearts from dummy. If East ruffs, he ruffs a loser, and if he does not, you can establish your jack of hearts for a club discard. (Had you played the top hearts from your hand, East could ruff and lead a trump, killing the dummy.)

Finally, if hearts do not break in a civilized manner, fall back on the club finesse.

KING-SIZE PROBLEM

East-West vulnerable

Dealer North

North

♠ 4 2
♥ K 10 8 7 6
♦ A J 5
♣ Q 4 3

South

♠ A Q 10 3
♥ A Q J 9 5
♦ 4
♣ A 8 2

North	South
Pass	1 ♥
3 ♥	6 ♥!
Pass	

The way you play you can afford to bid like that.

Opening lead: Three of diamonds

Plan the play. (Trumps are 2-1)

Solution

North

♠ 4 2
♥ K 10 8 7 6
♦ A J 5
♣ Q 4 3

West	East
♠ 8 7 5	♠ K J 9 6
♥ 2	♥ 4 3
♦ Q 9 8 3 2	♦ K 10 7 6
♣ J 9 7 6	♣ K 10 5

South

♠ A Q 10 3
♥ A Q J 9 5
♦ 4
♣ A 8 2

You should enter your hand at trick two with a trump (or a diamond ruff) and lead a *low club.* If West has the king of clubs, your are reduced to a simple finesse of the spade queen. However, if East has the king of clubs, you must resort to the double finesse in spades to rid yourself of your remaining club loser.

It is very important that you draw at most *one* trump before leading a club. If you make the mistake of drawing two rounds before leading a club and you find East with the king of clubs, you will have to use two additional trumps to get over to dummy to take the double spade finesse, and will find yourself one trick short even if both spade honors are onside! Help!

THE MEN FROM THE BOYS

North

♠ A Q 3 2
♥ K 6 5
♦ Q 3
♣ K 8 7 2

South

♠ 5 4
♥ A Q J 4 3
♦ J 8
♣ A 9 4 3

Contract: 4 ♥
Opening lead: Five of diamonds

East wins the ace and returns the deuce to West's king. At this point, East reaches for a match and drops his club holding face up on the table. You try not to look, but you can't help it. East has the Q J 10 6 in clubs. Being a good guy, you tell East to pick up his cards, and allow West to lead whatever he likes. West shifts to the five of clubs. (Also a nice guy.)

Under what circumstances can you still make this hand? Time limit: Two days.

Solution

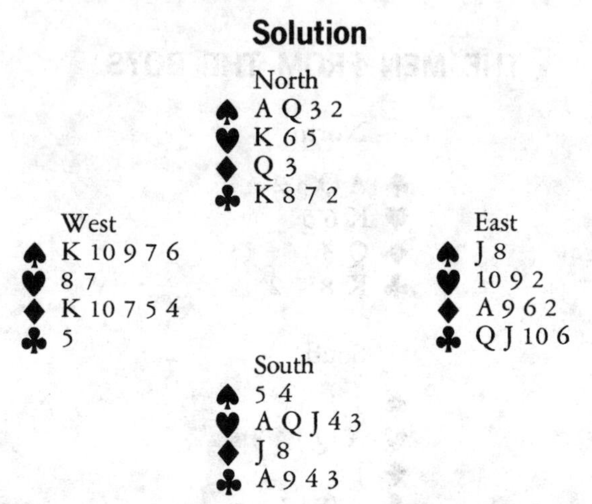

For openers, you must assume that West has the king of spades. Now you can concentrate on possible East distributions that will allow you to make the hand.

If East has four spades, playing four rounds of trumps after winning the ace of clubs will reduce him to six cards. Dummy will have four spades and Kx of clubs, and your hand will be two spades, a trump, and three clubs. What six cards can East hold? If he holds three spades and three clubs, a long spade can be established, and if he discards a club, that suit can be established. So you can make the hand if East started with four spades.

What if East is short in spades? All is not lost if East is either 3-3-3-4 or the actual distribution. Win the ace of clubs, finesse the queen of spades, cash the ace, and ruff a spade. Now the ace-king of trumps, leaving:

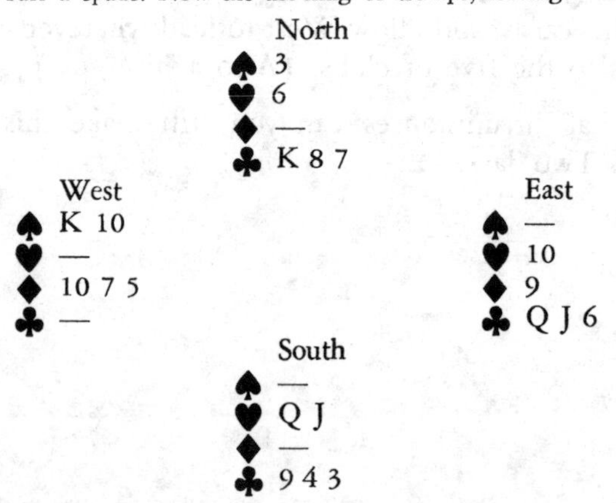

Dummy's last spade is led, squeezing East in three suits! If East discards a diamond, ruff, draw the last trump, and duck a club into East, who is endplayed in clubs.

If East sheds a club, ruff, and play the king and a club. East must either return a diamond, allowing you to ruff on the table and discard your last club, or play a trump, in which case your hand is high.

Finally, if East ruffs, overruff, and duck a club. East is endplayed.

THIRTY-THREE POINTS USUALLY PRODUCE A SLAM

Both sides vulnerable

Daeler South

North

♠ K 5 4
♥ K 5 4 3
♦ K 10
♣ K 6 5 4

South

♠ A Q
♥ A 6 2
♦. A 8 4 3 2
♣ A Q J

South	North
2 NT	3 ♣
3 ♦	6 NT
Pass	

Opening lead: Jack of spades

You win the ace and play off the ace, and queen of clubs, West discarding a spade on the second club. (If at any time you should happen to duck a trick in either red suit, a heart will be returned, so plan accordingly.) Plan the play.

Solution

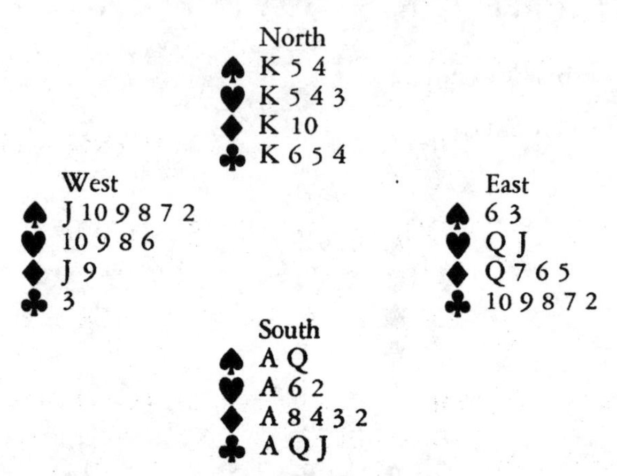

Your best play to develop a twelfth trick is to duck a trick in a red suit and hope for a red-suit squeeze, or a 3-3 division in the suit in which you have ducked a trick.

Because the diamond spots are better, you should concede a trick in diamonds by leading low to the ten *after* cashing a third club and a second spade.

This play wins anytime diamonds are 3-3 or West has specifically Q 9, J 9 or Q J xx.

Assuming the diamond loses to East and a heart is returned, win in dummy and play off your two remaining black suit winners, leaving:

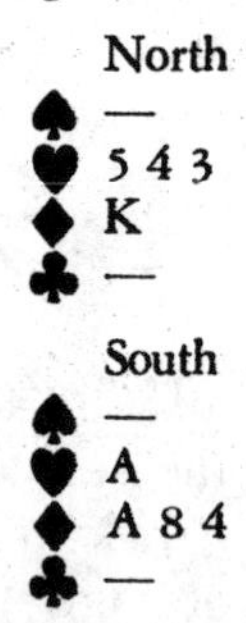

At this point, you will have to decide from the discards which red suit is good. For example, if West started with 4-4-4-1 distribution he will have had to discard three red cards, the third of which should be a giveaway.

On the other hand, if West started with six spades, your only hope is that diamonds were 3-3, or West had Q 9 or J 9 originally. In this case, cash the king of diamonds, enter your hand with a heart, and take the balance.

True, if West started with 5-3-4-1 distribution, you have ducked a trick in the wrong suit, but then again if West had 5-4-3-1, you ducked a trick in the right suit. Win some, lose some.

RATING SCALE

250-200	YOU SHOULD BE MAKING A LIVING FROM THE GAME
195-150	YOU SHOULD CONSIDER MAKING A LIVING FROM THE GAME
145-100	YOU SHOULD CONSIDER KEEPING YOUR PRESENT JOB
95-50	YOU SHOULD CONSIDER OTHER CARD GAMES
LESS	YOU SHOULD CONSIDER OTHER THINGS IN IN LIFE BESIDES CARDS

GRAND FINALE RATING SCALE

750-650	LET'S HOPE YOUR FRIENDS BELIEVE THIS
645-550	IMPRESSIVE
545-450	BUY MY NEXT QUIZ BOOK, YOU'LL DO BETTER
445-350	THINK ABOUT BUYING MY NEXT QUIZ BOOK
LESS	THINK ABOUT SELLING THIS BOOK

bridge conventions

A Guide to Understanding Techniques of Modern Bidding

Edwin B. Kantar

INDEX

CONVENTION TITLE	PAGES
STAYMAN	1 - 10
THE JACOBY TRANSFER BID	11 - 24
THE WEAK TWO BID	25 - 28
LIMIT RAISES	29 - 31
BLACKWOOD	32 - 36
THE WEAK JUMP OVERCALL	37 - 40
THE INTERMEDIATE JUMP OVERCALL	41 - 42
THE UNUSUAL NO TRUMP	43 - 50
STAYMAN AFTER A ONE NO TRUMP REBID	51 - 63
MICHAEL'S CUE BID	64 - 66
TOP AND BOTTOM CUE BID	67 - 68
THE WEISS CONVENTION	69 - 70
THE NEGATIVE DOUBLE	71 - 75
THE RESPONSIVE DOUBLE	76 - 80
THE FLANNERY TWO DIAMOND BID	81
THE FLANNERY TWO HEART BID	82
GERBER	83 - 85
DRURY	86 - 87
THE LIGHTNER SLAM DOUBLE	88 - 89
ASKING BIDS	90 - 91
FRAGMENT BIDS	92
ROTH-STONE ASTRO	93 - 95
OTHER CONVENTIONS OVER OPPONENT'S ONE NO TRUMP OPENING BID	96
THE GRAND SLAM FORCE	97 - 10
THE TWO CLUB OPENING BID	101 - 10
NON FORCING STAYMAN	107 - 10
TWO WAY STAYMAN	110 - 11
BLACKWOOD WITH A VOID	114 - 11
FLANNERY	116
GAMBLING THREE NO TRUMP OPENING BIDS	116 - 11
SPLINTER JUMPS	118 - 12
THE WESTERN CUE BID	125 - 12
FLINT	129 - 13
THE MILES CONVENTION	132 - 13

144 Pages . . . $7.00

The books listed above can be obtained from your book dealer or directly from Melvin Powe
When ordering, please remit $1.50 postage for the first book and 50¢ for each additional bo

Melvin Powers

12015 Sherman Road, No. Hollywood, California 91605

A PERSONAL WORD FROM MELVIN POWERS
PUBLISHER, WILSHIRE BOOK COMPANY

Dear Friend:

My goal is to publish interesting, informative, and inspirational books. You can help me accomplish this by answering the following questions, either by phone or by mail. Or, if convenient for you, I would welcome the opportunity to visit with you in my office and hear your comments in person.

Did you enjoy reading this book? Why?

Would you enjoy reading another similar book?

What idea in the book impressed you the most?

If applicable to your situation, have you incorporated this idea in your daily life?

Is there a chapter that could serve as a theme for an entire book? Please explain.

If you have an idea for a book, I would welcome discussing it with you. If you already have one in progress, write or call me concerning possible publication. I can be reached at (818) 765-8579.

Sincerely yours,
MELVIN POWERS

12015 Sherman Road
North Hollywood, California 91605

____ HOW TO WIN AT CHECKERS *Fred Reinfeld* 5.00
____ 1001 BRILLIANT WAYS TO CHECKMATE *Fred Reinfeld* 7.00
____ 1001 WINNING CHESS SACRIFICES & COMBINATIONS *Fred Reinfeld* 7.00

COOKERY & HERBS

____ CULPEPER'S HERBAL REMEDIES *Dr. Nicholas Culpeper* 5.00
____ FAST GOURMET COOKBOOK *Poppy Cannon* 2.50
____ HEALING POWER OF HERBS *May Bethel* 5.00
____ HEALING POWER OF NATURAL FOODS *May Bethel* 5.00
____ HERBS FOR HEALTH—HOW TO GROW & USE THEM *Louise Evans Doole* 5.00
____ HOME GARDEN COOKBOOK—DELICIOUS NATURAL FOOD RECIPES *Ken Kraft* 3.00
____ MEATLESS MEAL GUIDE *Tomi Ryan & James H. Ryan, M.D.* 4.00
____ VEGETABLE GARDENING FOR BEGINNERS *Hugh Wiberg* 2.00
____ VEGETABLES FOR TODAY'S GARDENS *R. Milton Carleton* 2.00
____ VEGETARIAN COOKERY *Janet Walker* 7.00
____ VEGETARIAN COOKING MADE EASY & DELECTABLE *Veronica Vezza* 3.00
____ VEGETARIAN DELIGHTS—A HAPPY COOKBOOK FOR HEALTH *K. R. Mehta* 2.00
____ VEGETARIAN GOURMET COOKBOOK *Joyce McKinnel* 3.00

GAMBLING & POKER

____ HOW TO WIN AT DICE GAMES *Skip Frey* 3.00
____ HOW TO WIN AT POKER *Terence Reese & Anthony T. Watkins* 7.00
____ WINNING AT CRAPS *Dr. Lloyd T. Commins* 5.00
____ WINNING AT GIN *Chester Wander & Cy Rice* 3.00
____ WINNING AT POKER—AN EXPERT'S GUIDE *John Archer* 5.00
____ WINNING AT 21—AN EXPERT'S GUIDE *John Archer* 5.00
____ WINNING POKER SYSTEMS *Norman Zadeh* 3.00

HEALTH

____ BEE POLLEN *Lynda Lyngheim & Jack Scagnetti* 3.00
____ COPING WITH ALZHEIMER'S *Rose Oliver, Ph.D. & Francis Bock, Ph.D.* 7.00
____ DR. LINDNER'S POINT SYSTEM FOOD PROGRAM *Peter G. Lindner, M.D.* 2.00
____ HELP YOURSELF TO BETTER SIGHT *Margaret Darst Corbett* 7.00
____ HOW YOU CAN STOP SMOKING PERMANENTLY *Ernest Caldwell* 5.00
____ MIND OVER PLATTER *Peter G. Lindner, M.D.* 5.00
____ NATURE'S WAY TO NUTRITION & VIBRANT HEALTH *Robert J. Scrutton* 3.00
____ NEW CARBOHYDRATE DIET COUNTER *Patti Lopez-Pereira* 2.00
____ REFLEXOLOGY *Dr. Maybelle Segal* 5.00
____ REFLEXOLOGY FOR GOOD HEALTH *Anna Kaye & Don C. Matchan* 5.00
____ 30 DAYS TO BEAUTIFUL LEGS *Dr. Marc Selner* 3.00
____ YOU CAN LEARN TO RELAX *Dr. Samuel Gutwirth* 3.00

HOBBIES

____ BEACHCOMBING FOR BEGINNERS *Norman Hickin* 2.00
____ BLACKSTONE'S MODERN CARD TRICKS *Harry Blackstone* 5.00
____ BLACKSTONE'S SECRETS OF MAGIC *Harry Blackstone* 5.00
____ COIN COLLECTING FOR BEGINNERS *Burton Hobson & Fred Reinfeld* 5.00
____ ENTERTAINING WITH ESP *Tony 'Doc' Shiels* 2.00
____ 400 FASCINATING MAGIC TRICKS YOU CAN DO *Howard Thurston* 5.00
____ HOW I TURN JUNK INTO FUN AND PROFIT *Sari* 3.00
____ HOW TO WRITE A HIT SONG & SELL IT *Tommy Boyce* 7.00
____ JUGGLING MADE EASY *Rudolf Dittrich* 3.00
____ MAGIC FOR ALL AGES *Walter Gibson* 4.00
____ MAGIC MADE EASY *Byron Wels* 2.00
____ STAMP COLLECTING FOR BEGINNERS *Burton Hobson* 3.00

HORSE PLAYER'S WINNING GUIDES

____ BETTING HORSES TO WIN *Les Conklin* 7.00
____ ELIMINATE THE LOSERS *Bob McKnight* 5.00
____ HOW TO PICK WINNING HORSES *Bob McKnight* 5.00

____ HOW TO WIN AT THE RACES *Sam (The Genius) Lewin* 5.00
____ HOW YOU CAN BEAT THE RACES *Jack Kavanagh* 5.00
____ MAKING MONEY AT THE RACES *David Barr* 5.00
____ PAYDAY AT THE RACES *Les Conklin* 5.00
____ SMART HANDICAPPING MADE EASY *William Bauman* 5.00
____ SUCCESS AT THE HARNESS RACES *Barry Meadow* 5.00
____ WINNING AT THE HARNESS RACES—AN EXPERT'S GUIDE *Nick Cammarano* 5.00

HUMOR

____ HOW TO FLATTEN YOUR TUSH *Coach Marge Reardon* 2.00
____ HOW TO MAKE LOVE TO YOURSELF *Ron Stevens & Joy Grdnic* 3.00
____ JOKE TELLER'S HANDBOOK *Bob Orben* 7.00
____ JOKES FOR ALL OCCASIONS *Al Schock* 5.00
____ 2,000 NEW LAUGHS FOR SPEAKERS *Bob Orben* 5.00
____ 2,400 JOKES TO BRIGHTEN YOUR SPEECHES *Robert Orben* 7.00
____ 2,500 JOKES TO START 'EM LAUGHING *Bob Orben* 7.00

HYPNOTISM

____ ADVANCED TECHNIQUES OF HYPNOSIS *Melvin Powers* 3.00
____ CHILDBIRTH WITH HYPNOSIS *William S. Kroger, M.D.* 5.00
____ HOW TO SOLVE YOUR SEX PROBLEMS WITH SELF-HYPNOSIS *Frank S. Caprio, M.D.* 5.00
____ HOW TO STOP SMOKING THRU SELF-HYPNOSIS *Leslie M. LeCron* 3.00
____ HOW YOU CAN BOWL BETTER USING SELF-HYPNOSIS *Jack Heise* 4.00
____ HOW YOU CAN PLAY BETTER GOLF USING SELF-HYPNOSIS *Jack Heise* 3.00
____ HYPNOSIS AND SELF-HYPNOSIS *Bernard Hollander, M.D.* 5.00
____ HYPNOTISM *(Originally published in 1893) Carl Sextus* 5.00
____ HYPNOTISM & PSYCHIC PHENOMENA *Simeon Edmunds* 4.00
____ HYPNOTISM MADE EASY *Dr. Ralph Winn* 5.00
____ HYPNOTISM MADE PRACTICAL *Louis Orton* 5.00
____ HYPNOTISM REVEALED *Melvin Powers* 3.00
____ HYPNOTISM TODAY *Leslie LeCron and Jean Bordeaux, Ph.D.* 5.00
____ MODERN HYPNOSIS *Lesley Kuhn & Salvatore Russo, Ph.D.* 5.00
____ NEW CONCEPTS OF HYPNOSIS *Bernard C. Gindes, M.D.* 7.00
____ NEW SELF-HYPNOSIS *Paul Adams* 7.00
____ POST-HYPNOTIC INSTRUCTIONS—SUGGESTIONS FOR THERAPY *Arnold Furst* 5.00
____ PRACTICAL GUIDE TO SELF-HYPNOSIS *Melvin Powers* 3.00
____ PRACTICAL HYPNOTISM *Philip Magonet, M.D.* 3.00
____ SECRETS OF HYPNOTISM *S. J. Van Pelt, M.D.* 5.00
____ SELF-HYPNOSIS—A CONDITIONED-RESPONSE TECHNIQUE *Laurence Sparks* 7.00
____ SELF-HYPNOSIS—ITS THEORY, TECHNIQUE & APPLICATION *Melvin Powers* 3.00
____ THERAPY THROUGH HYPNOSIS *Edited by Raphael H. Rhodes* 5.00

JUDAICA

____ SERVICE OF THE HEART *Evelyn Garfiel, Ph.D.* 7.00
____ STORY OF ISRAEL IN COINS *Jean & Maurice Gould* 2.00
____ STORY OF ISRAEL IN STAMPS *Maxim & Gabriel Shamir* 1.00
____ TONGUE OF THE PROPHETS *Robert St. John* 7.00

JUST FOR WOMEN

____ COSMOPOLITAN'S GUIDE TO MARVELOUS MEN Foreword by *Helen Gurley Brown* 3.00
____ COSMOPOLITAN'S HANG-UP HANDBOOK Foreword by *Helen Gurley Brown* 4.00
____ COSMOPOLITAN'S LOVE BOOK—A GUIDE TO ECSTASY IN BED 7.00
____ COSMOPOLITAN'S NEW ETIQUETTE GUIDE Foreword by *Helen Gurley Brown* 4.00
____ I AM A COMPLEAT WOMAN *Doris Hagopian & Karen O'Connor Sweeney* 3.00
____ JUST FOR WOMEN—A GUIDE TO THE FEMALE BODY *Richard E. Sand, M.D.* 5.00
____ NEW APPROACHES TO SEX IN MARRIAGE *John E. Eichenlaub, M.D.* 3.00
____ SEXUALLY ADEQUATE FEMALE *Frank S. Caprio, M.D.* 3.00
____ SEXUALLY FULFILLED WOMAN *Dr. Rachel Copelan* 5.00
____ YOUR FIRST YEAR OF MARRIAGE *Dr. Tom McGinnis* 3.00

MARRIAGE, SEX & PARENTHOOD

____ ABILITY TO LOVE *Dr. Allan Fromme* 7.00

____	GUIDE TO SUCCESSFUL MARRIAGE *Drs. Albert Ellis & Robert Harper*	7.00
____	HOW TO RAISE AN EMOTIONALLY HEALTHY, HAPPY CHILD *Albert Ellis, Ph.D.*	7.00
____	PARENT SURVIVAL TRAINING *Marvin Silverman, Ed.D. & David Lustig, Ph.D.*	10.00
____	SEX WITHOUT GUILT *Albert Ellis, Ph.D.*	5.00
____	SEXUALLY ADEQUATE MALE *Frank S. Caprio, M.D.*	3.00
____	SEXUALLY FULFILLED MAN *Dr. Rachel Copelan*	5.00
____	STAYING IN LOVE *Dr. Norton F. Kristy*	7.00
	MELVIN POWERS' MAIL ORDER LIBRARY	
____	HOW TO GET RICH IN MAIL ORDER *Melvin Powers*	20.00
____	HOW TO WRITE A GOOD ADVERTISEMENT *Victor O. Schwab*	20.00
____	MAIL ORDER MADE EASY *J. Frank Brumbaugh*	20.00
	METAPHYSICS & OCCULT	
____	BOOK OF TALISMANS, AMULETS & ZODIACAL GEMS *William Pavitt*	7.00
____	CONCENTRATION—A GUIDE TO MENTAL MASTERY *Mouni Sadhu*	7.00
____	EXTRA-TERRESTRIAL INTELLIGENCE—THE FIRST ENCOUNTER	6.00
____	FORTUNE TELLING WITH CARDS *P. Foli*	5.00
____	HOW TO INTERPRET DREAMS, OMENS & FORTUNE TELLING SIGNS *Gettings*	5.00
____	HOW TO UNDERSTAND YOUR DREAMS *Geoffrey A. Dudley*	5.00
____	IN DAYS OF GREAT PEACE *Mouni Sadhu*	3.00
____	MAGICIAN—HIS TRAINING AND WORK *W. E. Butler*	5.00
____	MEDITATION *Mouni Sadhu*	7.00
____	MODERN NUMEROLOGY *Morris C. Goodman*	5.00
____	NUMEROLOGY—ITS FACTS AND SECRETS *Ariel Yvon Taylor*	5.00
____	NUMEROLOGY MADE EASY *W. Mykian*	5.00
____	PALMISTRY MADE EASY *Fred Gettings*	5.00
____	PALMISTRY MADE PRACTICAL *Elizabeth Daniels Squire*	5.00
____	PALMISTRY SECRETS REVEALED *Henry Frith*	4.00
____	PROPHECY IN OUR TIME *Martin Ebon*	2.50
____	SUPERSTITION—ARE YOU SUPERSTITIOUS? *Eric Maple*	2.00
____	TAROT *Mouni Sadhu*	10.00
____	TAROT OF THE BOHEMIANS *Papus*	7.00
____	WAYS TO SELF-REALIZATION *Mouni Sadhu*	7.00
____	WITCHCRAFT, MAGIC & OCCULTISM—A FASCINATING HISTORY *W. B. Crow*	7.00
____	WITCHCRAFT—THE SIXTH SENSE *Justine Glass*	7.00
____	WORLD OF PSYCHIC RESEARCH *Hereward Carrington*	2.00
	SELF-HELP & INSPIRATIONAL	
____	CHARISMA—HOW TO GET "THAT SPECIAL MAGIC" *Marcia Grad*	7.00
____	DAILY POWER FOR JOYFUL LIVING *Dr. Donald Curtis*	7.00
____	DYNAMIC THINKING *Melvin Powers*	5.00
____	GREATEST POWER IN THE UNIVERSE *U. S. Andersen*	7.00
____	GROW RICH WHILE YOU SLEEP *Ben Sweetland*	7.00
____	GROWTH THROUGH REASON *Albert Ellis, Ph.D.*	7.00
____	GUIDE TO PERSONAL HAPPINESS *Albert Ellis, Ph.D. & Irving Becker, Ed.D.*	7.00
____	HANDWRITING ANALYSIS MADE EASY *John Marley*	7.00
____	HANDWRITING TELLS *Nadya Olyanova*	7.00
____	HOW TO ATTRACT GOOD LUCK *A.H.Z. Carr*	7.00
____	HOW TO BE GREAT *Dr. Donald Curtis*	5.00
____	HOW TO DEVELOP A WINNING PERSONALITY *Martin Panzer*	7.00
____	HOW TO DEVELOP AN EXCEPTIONAL MEMORY *Young & Gibson*	5.00
____	HOW TO LIVE WITH A NEUROTIC *Albert Ellis, Ph.D.*	7.00
____	HOW TO OVERCOME YOUR FEARS *M. P. Leahy, M.D.*	3.00
____	HOW TO SUCCEED *Brian Adams*	7.00
____	HUMAN PROBLEMS & HOW TO SOLVE THEM *Dr. Donald Curtis*	5.00
____	I CAN *Ben Sweetland*	7.00
____	I WILL *Ben Sweetland*	7.00
____	KNIGHT IN RUSTY ARMOR *Robert Fisher*	5.00
____	KNIGHT IN RUSTY ARMOR *Robert Fisher (Hard cover edition)*	10.00

_ LEFT-HANDED PEOPLE *Michael Barsley* 5.00
_ MAGIC IN YOUR MIND *U.S. Andersen* 7.00
_ MAGIC OF THINKING SUCCESS *Dr. David J. Schwartz* 7.00
_ MAGIC POWER OF YOUR MIND *Walter M. Germain* 7.00
_ MENTAL POWER THROUGH SLEEP SUGGESTION *Melvin Powers* 3.00
_ NEVER UNDERESTIMATE THE SELLING POWER OF A WOMAN *Dottie Walters* 7.00
_ NEW GUIDE TO RATIONAL LIVING *Albert Ellis, Ph.D. & R. Harper, Ph.D.* 7.00
_ PSYCHO-CYBERNETICS *Maxwell Maltz, M.D.* 7.00
_ PSYCHOLOGY OF HANDWRITING *Nadya Olyanova* 7.00
_ SALES CYBERNETICS *Brian Adams* 7.00
_ SCIENCE OF MIND IN DAILY LIVING *Dr. Donald Curtis* 7.00
_ SECRET OF SECRETS *U.S. Andersen* 7.00
_ SECRET POWER OF THE PYRAMIDS *U. S. Andersen* 7.00
_ SELF-THERAPY FOR THE STUTTERER *Malcolm Frazer* 3.00
_ SUCCESS-CYBERNETICS *U. S. Andersen* 7.00
_ 10 DAYS TO A GREAT NEW LIFE *William E. Edwards* 3.00
_ THINK AND GROW RICH *Napoleon Hill* 7.00
_ THREE MAGIC WORDS *U. S. Andersen* 7.00
_ TREASURY OF COMFORT *Edited by Rabbi Sidney Greenberg* 7.00
_ TREASURY OF THE ART OF LIVING *Sidney S. Greenberg* 7.00
_ WHAT YOUR HANDWRITING REVEALS *Albert E. Hughes* 4.00
_ YOUR SUBCONSCIOUS POWER *Charles M. Simmons* 7.00
_ YOUR THOUGHTS CAN CHANGE YOUR LIFE *Dr. Donald Curtis* 7.00

SPORTS

_ BICYCLING FOR FUN AND GOOD HEALTH *Kenneth E. Luther* 2.00
_ BILLIARDS—POCKET • CAROM • THREE CUSHION *Clive Cottingham, Jr.* 5.00
_ COMPLETE GUIDE TO FISHING *Vlad Evanoff* 2.00
_ HOW TO IMPROVE YOUR RACQUETBALL *Lubarsky, Kaufman & Scagnetti* 5.00
_ HOW TO WIN AT POCKET BILLIARDS *Edward D. Knuchell* 7.00
_ JOY OF WALKING *Jack Scagnetti* 3.00
_ LEARNING & TEACHING SOCCER SKILLS *Eric Worthington* 3.00
_ MOTORCYCLING FOR BEGINNERS *I.G. Edmonds* 3.00
_ RACQUETBALL FOR WOMEN *Toni Hudson, Jack Scagnetti & Vince Rondone* 3.00
_ RACQUETBALL MADE EASY *Steve Lubarsky, Rod Delson & Jack Scagnetti* 5.00
_ SECRET OF BOWLING STRIKES *Dawson Taylor* 5.00
_ SECRET OF PERFECT PUTTING *Horton Smith & Dawson Taylor* 5.00
_ SOCCER—THE GAME & HOW TO PLAY IT *Gary Rosenthal* 7.00
_ STARTING SOCCER *Edward F. Dolan, Jr.* 5.00

TENNIS LOVER'S LIBRARY

_ BEGINNER'S GUIDE TO WINNING TENNIS *Helen Hull Jacobs* 2.00
_ HOW TO BEAT BETTER TENNIS PLAYERS *Loring Fiske* 4.00
_ PSYCH YOURSELF TO BETTER TENNIS *Dr. Walter A. Luszki* 2.00
_ TENNIS FOR BEGINNERS *Dr. H. A. Murray* 2.00
_ TENNIS MADE EASY *Joel Brecheen* 5.00
_ WEEKEND TENNIS—HOW TO HAVE FUN & WIN AT THE SAME TIME *Bill Talbert* 3.00

WILSHIRE PET LIBRARY

_ DOG TRAINING MADE EASY & FUN *John W. Kellogg* 5.00
_ HOW TO BRING UP YOUR PET DOG *Kurt Unkelbach* 2.00
_ HOW TO RAISE & TRAIN YOUR PUPPY *Jeff Griffen* 5.00

books listed above can be obtained from your book dealer or directly from Melvin Powers.
en ordering, please remit $1.50 postage for the first book and 50¢ for each additional book.

Melvin Powers
12015 Sherman Road, No. Hollywood, California 91605

Notes

Notes

Notes

Notes

Notes